# Knit & Crochet Planner

## by Kristen Mangus

### Project pages and tracking sheets
### for knitters and crocheters

# GoodKnit Kisses

# Knit & Crochet Planner

Kristen Mangus
GoodKnit Kisses
Copyright © 2019 Kristen Mangus
All rights reserved.

Book Design by Joann Gay
Photography by Kristen Mangus
Charts & Graphics by Joann Gay
Cover by Joann Gay
Modeling by Morgan Mangus and Megan Mangus

Acknowledgements:
I'd like to thank my GKK Team, Carol Blakeley and Joann Gay. They've been instrumental in getting this book published by compiling information, acting as a sounding board for ideas and putting all my thoughts into written form.

Dedication:
This workbook is dedicated to all those that love yarn, especially the followers and supporters of me and of GoodKnit Kisses. (And a special shoutout to all my loom knitters!)

PUBLISHED BY:
GoodKnit Kisses

REQUESTS FOR INFORMATION:
GoodKnit Kisses
PO Box 90
Keller, TX 76244

Industry Standards & Guidelines Source:
Craft Yarn Council www.craftyarncouncil.com
Used by permission with credit given. All rights reserved.

# PROJECT PAGE

## PROJECT

Name: _____    Start Date: _____

Made for: _____    End Date: _____

## PATTERN

Pattern: _____

Source: _____
          (Website / Book / Magazine)

Gauge: _____ sts X _____ rows in _____ in/cm

Size: _____

## YARN

| Name | Color | # Skeins /Yds |
|------|-------|---------------|
|      |       |               |
|      |       |               |
|      |       |               |
|      |       |               |

Attach Yarn Label(s) Here

## MATERIALS

### Needle/Hook/Loom

| Name/Brand/Style | Size |
|------------------|------|
|                  |      |
|                  |      |
|                  |      |
|                  |      |

### Other Materials

| ◯ tapestry needle | ◯ |
|-------------------|---|
| ◯ stitch marker(s) _____ | ◯ |
| ◯ | ◯ |

Remove this page and keep it with your project for a quick reference.

Knit & Crochet Planner          goodknitkisses.com

# PROJECT NOTES

_____

_____

_____

_____

_____

_____

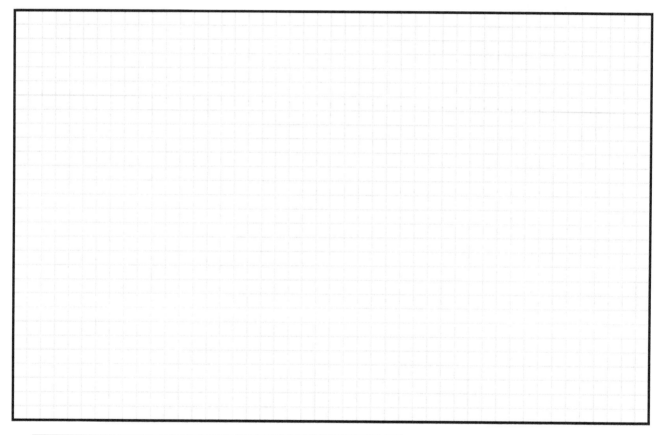

| Loom-Needle-Hook Equivalence Chart with Recommended Yarn Weight | | | | | | | | |
|---|---|---|---|---|---|---|---|---|
| Loom Size | | Needle Size | | Hook Size | | Yarn Weight | | |
| Gauge | Peg C2C (in.) | US | mm | US | mm | US | UK/AU | Avg. sts/in |
| EFG | 3/16 | 1-3 | 2.25-3.25mm | A-D | 2-3.125mm | 0-2 | 1-3 ply | 7-8 |
| FG | 1/4 | 3-6 | 3.25-4mm | D-G | 3.125-4.25mm | 1-3 | 2,4 & 8-ply | 5-7 |
| SG | 5/16, 3/8, 7/16 | 5-8 | 3.75-5mm | F-H | 3.75-5mm | 2-4 | 2,4 & 8-ply, DK | 4-5 |
| RG | 1/2, 9/16 | 8-10 | 5-6mm | H-J | 5-5.75mm | 4-5 | 8-12-ply/DK/Aran | 3-4 |
| LG | 5/8, 11/16 | 10-13 | 6-9mm | J-M | 5.75-9mm | 5-6 | 10-12-ply/Aran/Chunky | 2-3 |
| XLG | 3/4, 13/16, 7/8, 15/16 | 13-15 | 9-10mm | M-N+ | 9-10mm | 6-7 | 12-ply/Chunky | 1.5-3 |
| JUMBO | +/- 1 1/2 | 19-35 | 12.75-20+mm | M-Q+ | 9-30+mm | 6-7 | Chunky/Roving | .75-1 |

**EFG**: Extra Fine Gauge | **FG**: Fine Gauge | **SG**: Small Gauge | **RG**: Regular Gauge | **LG**: Large Gauge | **XLG**: Extra Large Gauge | **JUMBO**: Jumbo

Knit & Crochet Planner  goodknitkisses.com

# PROJECT PAGE

## PROJECT

Name: _____    Start Date: _____

Made for: _____    End Date: _____

## PATTERN

Pattern: _____

Source: _____
(Website / Book / Magazine)

Gauge: _____ sts X _____ rows in _____ in/cm

Size: _____

## YARN

| Name | Color | # Skeins /Yds |
|------|-------|---------------|
|      |       |               |
|      |       |               |
|      |       |               |
|      |       |               |

Attach Yarn Label(s) Here

## MATERIALS

### Needle/Hook/Loom

| Name/Brand/Style | Size |
|------------------|------|
|                  |      |
|                  |      |
|                  |      |
|                  |      |

### Other Materials

| | |
|--|--|
| ◯ tapestry needle | ◯ |
| ◯ stitch marker(s) _____ | ◯ |
| ◯ | ◯ |

Remove this page and keep it with your project for a quick reference.

Knit & Crochet Planner          goodknitkisses.com

## PROJECT NOTES

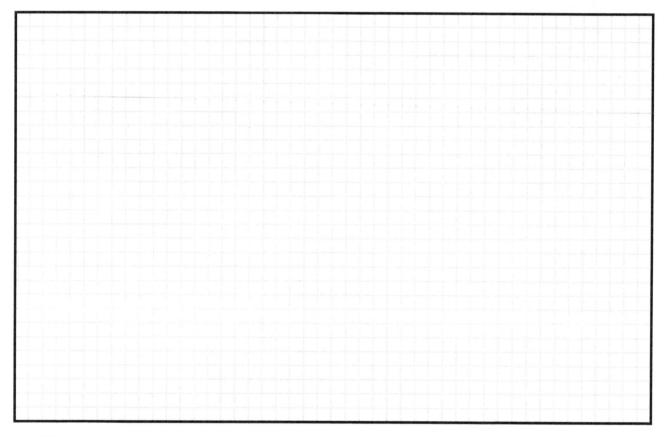

| Loom-Needle-Hook Equivalence Chart with Recommended Yarn Weight | | | | | | | | |
|---|---|---|---|---|---|---|---|---|
| Loom Size | | Needle Size | | Hook Size | | Yarn Weight | | |
| Gauge | Peg C2C (in.) | US | mm | US | mm | US | UK/AU | Avg. sts/in |
| EFG | ³⁄₁₆ | 1-3 | 2.25-3.25mm | A-D | 2-3.125mm | 0-2 | 1-3 ply | 7-8 |
| FG | ¼ | 3-6 | 3.25-4mm | D-G | 3.125-4.25mm | 1-3 | 2,4 & 8-ply | 5-7 |
| SG | ⁵⁄₁₆, ³⁄₈, ⁷⁄₁₆ | 5-8 | 3.75-5mm | F-H | 3.75-5mm | 2-4 | 2,4 & 8-ply,DK | 4-5 |
| RG | ½, ⁹⁄₁₆ | 8-10 | 5-6mm | H-J | 5-5.75mm | 4-5 | 8-12-ply/DK/Aran | 3-4 |
| LG | ⁵⁄₈, ¹¹⁄₁₆ | 10-13 | 6-9mm | J-M | 5.75-9mm | 5-6 | 10-12-ply/Aran/Chunky | 2-3 |
| XLG | ³⁄₄, ¹³⁄₁₆, ⁷⁄₈, ¹⁵⁄₁₆ | 13-15 | 9-10mm | M-N+ | 9-10mm | 6-7 | 12-ply/Chunky | 1.5-3 |
| JUMBO | +/- 1½ | 19-35 | 12.75-20+mm | M-Q+ | 9-30+mm | 6-7 | Chunky/Roving | .75-1 |

**EFG**: Extra Fine Gauge | **FG**: Fine Gauge | **SG**: Small Gauge |**RG**: Regular Gauge | **LG**: Large Gauge | **XLG**: Extra Large Gauge | **JUMBO**: Jumbo

Knit & Crochet Planner    goodknitkisses.com

# PROJECT PAGE

## PROJECT

Name: _____     Start Date: _____

Made for: _____     End Date: _____

## PATTERN

Pattern: _____

Source: _____
(Website / Book / Magazine)

Gauge: ____ sts X ____ rows in _____ in/cm

Size: _____

## YARN

| Name | Color | # Skeins /Yds |
|------|-------|---------------|
|      |       |               |
|      |       |               |
|      |       |               |
|      |       |               |

Attach Yarn Label(s) Here

## MATERIALS

### Needle/Hook/Loom

| Name/Brand/Style | Size |
|------------------|------|
|                  |      |
|                  |      |
|                  |      |
|                  |      |

### Other Materials

| | |
|---|---|
| ◯ tapestry needle | ◯ |
| ◯ stitch marker(s) _____ | ◯ |
| ◯ | ◯ |

Remove this page and keep it with your project for a quick reference.

Knit & Crochet Planner          goodknitkisses.com

## PROJECT NOTES

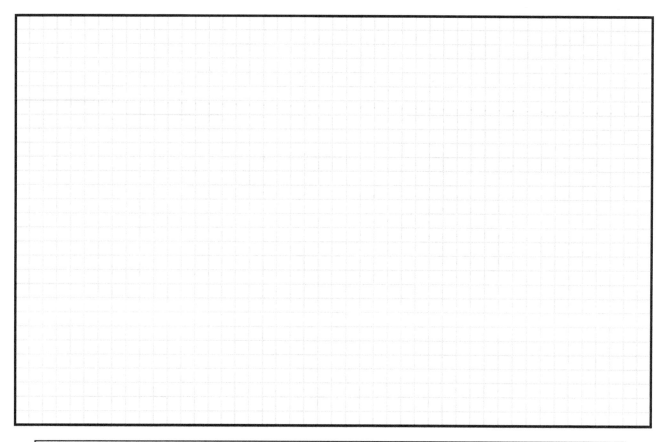

| Loom-Needle-Hook Equivalence Chart with Recommended Yarn Weight | | | | | | | | |
|---|---|---|---|---|---|---|---|---|
| Loom Size | | Needle Size | | Hook Size | | Yarn Weight | | |
| Gauge | Peg C2C (in.) | US | mm | US | mm | US | UK/AU | Avg. sts/in |
| EFG | $\frac{3}{16}$ | 1-3 | 2.25-3.25mm | A-D | 2-3.125mm | 0-2 | 1-3 ply | 7-8 |
| FG | $\frac{1}{4}$ | 3-6 | 3.25-4mm | D-G | 3.125-4.25mm | 1-3 | 2,4 & 8-ply | 5-7 |
| SG | $\frac{5}{16}$, $\frac{3}{8}$, $\frac{7}{16}$ | 5-8 | 3.75-5mm | F-H | 3.75-5mm | 2-4 | 2,4 & 8-ply,DK | 4-5 |
| RG | $\frac{1}{2}$, $\frac{9}{16}$ | 8-10 | 5-6mm | H-J | 5-5.75mm | 4-5 | 8-12-ply/DK/Aran | 3-4 |
| LG | $\frac{5}{8}$, $\frac{11}{16}$ | 10-13 | 6-9mm | J-M | 5.75-9mm | 5-6 | 10-12-ply/Aran/Chunky | 2-3 |
| XLG | $\frac{3}{4}$, $\frac{13}{16}$, $\frac{7}{8}$, $\frac{15}{16}$ | 13-15 | 9-10mm | M-N+ | 9-10mm | 6-7 | 12-ply/Chunky | 1.5-3 |
| JUMBO | +/- $1\frac{1}{2}$ | 19-35 | 12.75-20+mm | M-Q+ | 9-30+mm | 6-7 | Chunky/Roving | .75-1 |

**EFG**: Extra Fine Gauge | **FG**: Fine Gauge | **SG**: Small Gauge | **RG**: Regular Gauge | **LG**: Large Gauge | **XLG**: Extra Large Gauge | **JUMBO**: Jumbo

Knit & Crochet Planner  goodknitkisses.com

# PROJECT PAGE

## PROJECT

Name: _____          Start Date: _____

Made for: _____          End Date: _____

## PATTERN

Pattern: _____

Source: _____
(Website / Book / Magazine)

Gauge: ____ sts X ____ rows in _____ in/cm

Size: _____

## YARN

| Name | Color | # Skeins /Yds |
|------|-------|---------------|
|      |       |               |
|      |       |               |
|      |       |               |
|      |       |               |

Attach Yarn Label(s) Here

## MATERIALS

### Needle/Hook/Loom

| Name/Brand/Style | Size |
|------------------|------|
|                  |      |
|                  |      |
|                  |      |
|                  |      |

### Other Materials

| | |
|---|---|
| ◯ tapestry needle | ◯ |
| ◯ stitch marker(s) _____ | ◯ |
| ◯ | ◯ |

Remove this page and keep it with your project for a quick reference.

# PROJECT NOTES

PROJECT

_____

_____

_____

_____

_____

_____

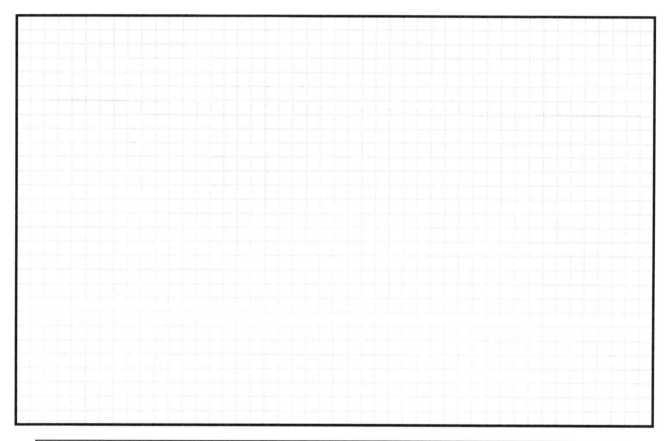

| Loom-Needle-Hook Equivalence Chart with Recommended Yarn Weight | | | | | | | | |
|---|---|---|---|---|---|---|---|---|
| Loom Size | | Needle Size | | Hook Size | | Yarn Weight | | |
| Gauge | Peg C2C (in.) | US | mm | US | mm | US | UK/AU | Avg. sts/in |
| EFG | $\frac{3}{16}$ | 1-3 | 2.25-3.25mm | A-D | 2-3.125mm | 0-2 | 1-3 ply | 7-8 |
| FG | $\frac{1}{4}$ | 3-6 | 3.25-4mm | D-G | 3.125-4.25mm | 1-3 | 2,4 & 8-ply | 5-7 |
| SG | $\frac{5}{16}$, $\frac{3}{8}$, $\frac{7}{16}$ | 5-8 | 3.75-5mm | F-H | 3.75-5mm | 2-4 | 2,4 & 8-ply,DK | 4-5 |
| RG | $\frac{1}{2}$, $\frac{9}{16}$ | 8-10 | 5-6mm | H-J | 5-5.75mm | 4-5 | 8-12-ply/DK/Aran | 3-4 |
| LG | $\frac{5}{8}$, $\frac{11}{16}$ | 10-13 | 6-9mm | J-M | 5.75-9mm | 5-6 | 10-12-ply/Aran/Chunky | 2-3 |
| XLG | $\frac{3}{4}$, $\frac{13}{16}$, $\frac{7}{8}$, $\frac{15}{16}$ | 13-15 | 9-10mm | M-N+ | 9-10mm | 6-7 | 12-ply/Chunky | 1.5-3 |
| JUMBO | +/- $1\frac{1}{2}$ | 19-35 | 12.75-20+mm | M-Q+ | 9-30+mm | 6-7 | Chunky/Roving | .75-1 |

**EFG**: Extra Fine Gauge | **FG**: Fine Gauge | **SG**: Small Gauge |**RG**: Regular Gauge | **LG**: Large Gauge | **XLG**: Extra Large Gauge | **JUMBO**: Jumbo

Knit & Crochet Planner              goodknitkisses.com

# PROJECT PAGE

## PROJECT

Name: _____          Start Date: _____

Made for: _____       End Date: _____

## PATTERN

Pattern: _____

Source: _____
(Website / Book / Magazine)

Gauge: _____ sts X _____ rows in _____ in/cm

Size: _____

## YARN

| Name | Color | # Skeins /Yds |
|------|-------|---------------|
|      |       |               |
|      |       |               |
|      |       |               |
|      |       |               |

Attach Yarn Label(s) Here

## MATERIALS

### Needle/Hook/Loom

| Name/Brand/Style | Size |
|------------------|------|
|                  |      |
|                  |      |
|                  |      |
|                  |      |

### Other Materials

| | |
|---|---|
| ◯ tapestry needle | ◯ |
| ◯ stitch marker(s) _____ | ◯ |
| ◯ | ◯ |

Remove this page and keep it with your project for a quick reference.

Knit & Crochet Planner                    goodknitkisses.com

PROJECT

# PROJECT NOTES

_____

_____

_____

_____

_____

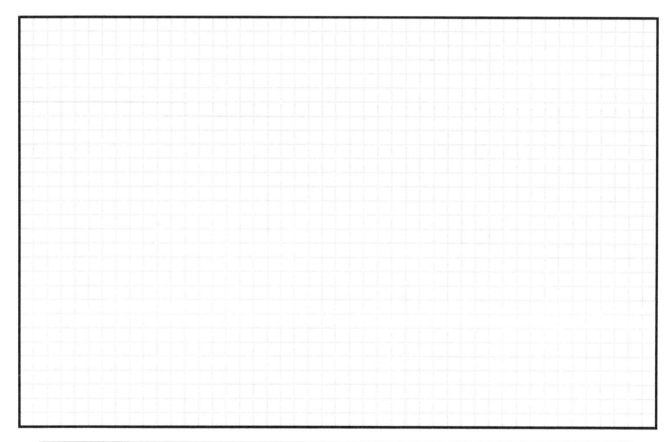

| Loom-Needle-Hook Equivalence Chart with Recommended Yarn Weight | | | | | | | | |
|---|---|---|---|---|---|---|---|---|
| Loom Size | | Needle Size | | Hook Size | | Yarn Weight | | |
| Gauge | Peg C2C (in.) | US | mm | US | mm | US | UK/AU | Avg. sts/in |
| EFG | $^3/_{16}$ | 1-3 | 2.25-3.25mm | A-D | 2-3.125mm | 0-2 | 1-3 ply | 7-8 |
| FG | $^1/_4$ | 3-6 | 3.25-4mm | D-G | 3.125-4.25mm | 1-3 | 2,4 & 8-ply | 5-7 |
| SG | $^5/_{16}, ^3/_8, ^7/_{16}$ | 5-8 | 3.75-5mm | F-H | 3.75-5mm | 2-4 | 2,4 & 8-ply,DK | 4-5 |
| RG | $^1/_2, ^9/_{16}$ | 8-10 | 5-6mm | H-J | 5-5.75mm | 4-5 | 8-12-ply/DK/Aran | 3-4 |
| LG | $^5/_8, ^{11}/_{16}$ | 10-13 | 6-9mm | J-M | 5.75-9mm | 5-6 | 10-12-ply/Aran/Chunky | 2-3 |
| XLG | $^3/_4, ^{13}/_{16}, ^7/_8, ^{15}/_{16}$ | 13-15 | 9-10mm | M-N+ | 9-10mm | 6-7 | 12-ply/Chunky | 1.5-3 |
| JUMBO | +/- $1^1/_2$ | 19-35 | 12.75-20+mm | M-Q+ | 9-30+mm | 6-7 | Chunky/Roving | .75-1 |

**EFG**: Extra Fine Gauge | **FG**: Fine Gauge | **SG**: Small Gauge |**RG**: Regular Gauge | **LG**: Large Gauge | **XLG**: Extra Large Gauge | **JUMBO**: Jumbo

Knit & Crochet Planner            goodknitkisses.com

# PROJECT PAGE

## PROJECT

Name: _____  Start Date: _____

Made for: _____  End Date: _____

## PATTERN

Pattern: _____

Source: _____
(Website / Book / Magazine)

Gauge: ____ sts X ____ rows in _____ in/cm

Size: _____

## YARN

| Name | Color | # Skeins /Yds |
|------|-------|---------------|
|      |       |               |
|      |       |               |
|      |       |               |
|      |       |               |

Attach Yarn Label(s) Here

## MATERIALS

### Needle/Hook/Loom

| Name/Brand/Style | Size |
|------------------|------|
|                  |      |
|                  |      |
|                  |      |
|                  |      |

### Other Materials

| | |
|---|---|
| ◯ tapestry needle | ◯ |
| ◯ stitch marker(s) _____ | ◯ |
| ◯ | ◯ |

Remove this page and keep it with your project for a quick reference.

Knit & Crochet Planner    goodknitkisses.com

## PROJECT NOTES

_____

_____

_____

_____

_____

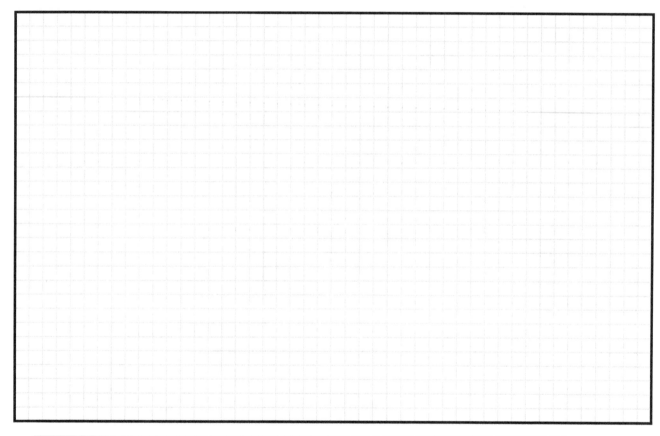

| Loom-Needle-Hook Equivalence Chart with Recommended Yarn Weight | | | | | | | | |
|---|---|---|---|---|---|---|---|---|
| Loom Size | | Needle Size | | Hook Size | | Yarn Weight | | |
| Gauge | Peg C2C (in.) | US | mm | US | mm | US | UK/AU | Avg. sts/in |
| EFG | $^3/_{16}$ | 1-3 | 2.25-3.25mm | A-D | 2-3.125mm | 0-2 | 1-3 ply | 7-8 |
| FG | $^1/_4$ | 3-6 | 3.25-4mm | D-G | 3.125-4.25mm | 1-3 | 2,4 & 8-ply | 5-7 |
| SG | $^5/_{16}$, $^3/_8$, $^7/_{16}$ | 5-8 | 3.75-5mm | F-H | 3.75-5mm | 2-4 | 2,4 & 8-ply, DK | 4-5 |
| RG | $^1/_2$, $^9/_{16}$ | 8-10 | 5-6mm | H-J | 5-5.75mm | 4-5 | 8-12-ply/DK/Aran | 3-4 |
| LG | $^5/_8$, $^{11}/_{16}$ | 10-13 | 6-9mm | J-M | 5.75-9mm | 5-6 | 10-12-ply/Aran/Chunky | 2-3 |
| XLG | $^3/_4$, $^{13}/_{16}$, $^7/_8$, $^{15}/_{16}$ | 13-15 | 9-10mm | M-N+ | 9-10mm | 6-7 | 12-ply/Chunky | 1.5-3 |
| JUMBO | +/- $1^1/_2$ | 19-35 | 12.75-20+mm | M-Q+ | 9-30+mm | 6-7 | Chunky/Roving | .75-1 |

**EFG**: Extra Fine Gauge | **FG**: Fine Gauge | **SG**: Small Gauge | **RG**: Regular Gauge | **LG**: Large Gauge | **XLG**: Extra Large Gauge | **JUMBO**: Jumbo

Knit & Crochet Planner          goodknitkisses.com

## PROJECT

Name: _____     Start Date: _____

Made for: _____     End Date: _____

## PATTERN

Pattern: _____

Source: _____
(Website / Book / Magazine)

Gauge: _____ sts X _____ rows in _____ in/cm

Size: _____

## YARN

| Name | Color | # Skeins /Yds |
|------|-------|---------------|
|      |       |               |
|      |       |               |
|      |       |               |
|      |       |               |

Attach Yarn Label(s) Here

## MATERIALS

### Needle/Hook/Loom

| Name/Brand/Style | Size |
|------------------|------|
|                  |      |
|                  |      |
|                  |      |
|                  |      |

### Other Materials

| | |
|---|---|
| ◯ tapestry needle | ◯ |
| ◯ stitch marker(s) _____ | ◯ |
| ◯ | ◯ |

Remove this page and keep it with your project for a quick reference.

Knit & Crochet Planner          goodknitkisses.com

## PROJECT NOTES

_____

_____

_____

_____

_____

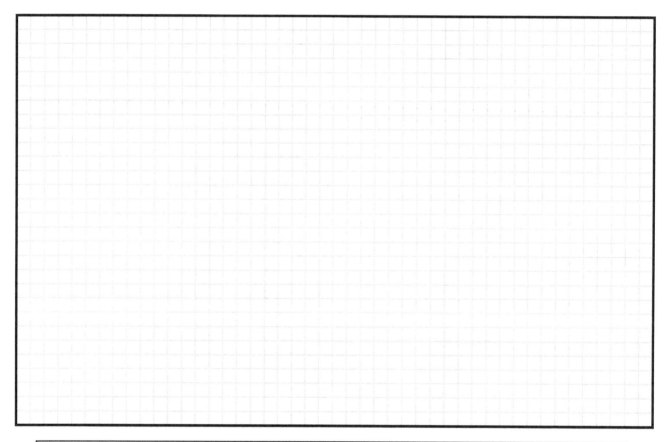

| Loom-Needle-Hook Equivalence Chart with Recommended Yarn Weight | | | | | | | | |
|---|---|---|---|---|---|---|---|---|
| Loom Size | | Needle Size | | Hook Size | | Yarn Weight | | |
| Gauge | Peg C2C (in.) | US | mm | US | mm | US | UK/AU | Avg. sts/in |
| EFG | $^3/_{16}$ | 1-3 | 2.25-3.25mm | A-D | 2-3.125mm | 0-2 | 1-3 ply | 7-8 |
| FG | $^1/_4$ | 3-6 | 3.25-4mm | D-G | 3.125-4.25mm | 1-3 | 2,4 & 8-ply | 5-7 |
| SG | $^5/_{16}$, $^3/_8$, $^7/_{16}$ | 5-8 | 3.75-5mm | F-H | 3.75-5mm | 2-4 | 2,4 & 8-ply,DK | 4-5 |
| RG | $^1/_2$, $^9/_{16}$ | 8-10 | 5-6mm | H-J | 5-5.75mm | 4-5 | 8-12-ply/DK/Aran | 3-4 |
| LG | $^5/_8$, $^{11}/_{16}$ | 10-13 | 6-9mm | J-M | 5.75-9mm | 5-6 | 10-12-ply/Aran/Chunky | 2-3 |
| XLG | $^3/_4$, $^{13}/_{16}$, $^7/_8$, $^{15}/_{16}$ | 13-15 | 9-10mm | M-N+ | 9-10mm | 6-7 | 12-ply/Chunky | 1.5-3 |
| JUMBO | +/- $1^1/_2$ | 19-35 | 12.75-20+mm | M-Q+ | 9-30+mm | 6-7 | Chunky/Roving | .75-1 |

**EFG**: Extra Fine Gauge | **FG**: Fine Gauge | **SG**: Small Gauge | **RG**: Regular Gauge | **LG**: Large Gauge | **XLG**: Extra Large Gauge | **JUMBO**: Jumbo

Knit & Crochet Planner        goodknitkisses.com

# PROJECT PAGE

## PROJECT

Name: _____          Start Date: _____

Made for: _____          End Date: _____

## PATTERN

Pattern: _____

Source: _____
(Website / Book / Magazine)

Gauge: _____ sts X _____ rows in _____ in/cm

Size: _____

## YARN

| Name | Color | # Skeins /Yds |
|------|-------|---------------|
|      |       |               |
|      |       |               |
|      |       |               |
|      |       |               |

Attach Yarn Label(s) Here

## MATERIALS

### Needle/Hook/Loom

| Name/Brand/Style | Size |
|------------------|------|
|                  |      |
|                  |      |
|                  |      |
|                  |      |

### Other Materials

| | |
|---|---|
| ◯ tapestry needle | ◯ |
| ◯ stitch marker(s) _____ | ◯ |
| ◯ | ◯ |

Remove this page and keep it with your project for a quick reference.

Knit & Crochet Planner          goodknitkisses.com

## PROJECT NOTES

_____

_____

_____

_____

_____

_____

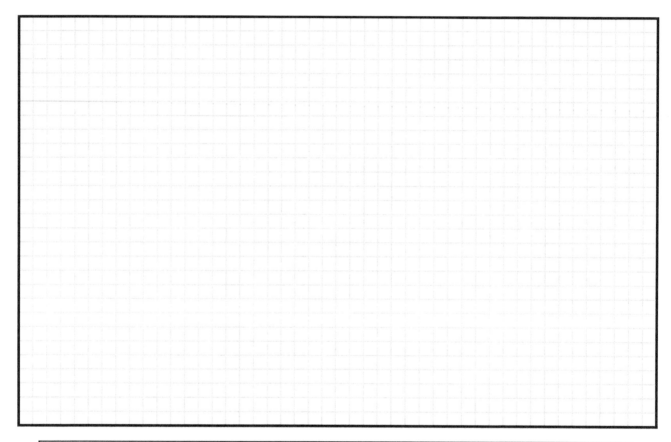

| Loom-Needle-Hook Equivalence Chart with Recommended Yarn Weight | | | | | | | | |
|---|---|---|---|---|---|---|---|---|
| Loom Size | | Needle Size | | Hook Size | | Yarn Weight | | |
| Gauge | Peg C2C (in.) | US | mm | US | mm | US | UK/AU | Avg. sts/in |
| EFG | $^3/_{16}$ | 1-3 | 2.25-3.25mm | A-D | 2-3.125mm | 0-2 | 1-3 ply | 7-8 |
| FG | $^1/_4$ | 3-6 | 3.25-4mm | D-G | 3.125-4.25mm | 1-3 | 2,4 & 8-ply | 5-7 |
| SG | $^5/_{16}$, $^3/_8$, $^7/_{16}$ | 5-8 | 3.75-5mm | F-H | 3.75-5mm | 2-4 | 2,4 & 8-ply, DK | 4-5 |
| RG | $^1/_2$, $^9/_{16}$ | 8-10 | 5-6mm | H-J | 5-5.75mm | 4-5 | 8-12-ply/DK/Aran | 3-4 |
| LG | $^5/_8$, $^{11}/_{16}$ | 10-13 | 6-9mm | J-M | 5.75-9mm | 5-6 | 10-12-ply/Aran/Chunky | 2-3 |
| XLG | $^3/_4$, $^{13}/_{16}$, $^7/_8$, $^{15}/_{16}$ | 13-15 | 9-10mm | M-N+ | 9-10mm | 6-7 | 12-ply/Chunky | 1.5-3 |
| JUMBO | +/- 1$^1/_2$ | 19-35 | 12.75-20+mm | M-Q+ | 9-30+mm | 6-7 | Chunky/Roving | .75-1 |

**EFG**: Extra Fine Gauge | **FG**: Fine Gauge | **SG**: Small Gauge |**RG**: Regular Gauge | **LG**: Large Gauge | **XLG**: Extra Large Gauge | **JUMBO**: Jumbo

Knit & Crochet Planner            goodknitkisses.com

# PROJECT PAGE

## PROJECT

Name: _____   Start Date: _____

Made for: _____   End Date: _____

## PATTERN

Pattern: _____

Source: _____
(Website / Book / Magazine)

Gauge: _____ sts X _____ rows in _____ in/cm

Size: _____

## YARN

| Name | Color | # Skeins /Yds |
|------|-------|---------------|
|      |       |               |
|      |       |               |
|      |       |               |
|      |       |               |

Attach Yarn Label(s) Here

## MATERIALS

### Needle/Hook/Loom

| Name/Brand/Style | Size |
|------------------|------|
|                  |      |
|                  |      |
|                  |      |
|                  |      |

### Other Materials

| ○ tapestry needle | ○ |
|-------------------|---|
| ○ stitch marker(s) _____ | ○ |
| ○ | ○ |

Remove this page and keep it with your project for a quick reference.

Knit & Crochet Planner          goodknitkisses.com

## PROJECT NOTES

_____

_____

_____

_____

_____

_____

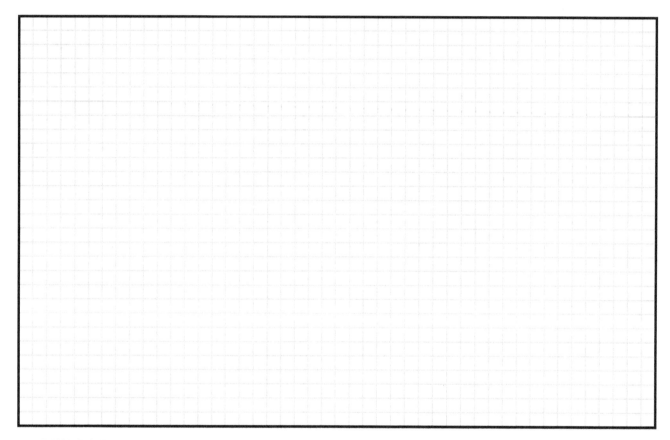

| Loom-Needle-Hook Equivalence Chart with Recommended Yarn Weight | | | | | | | | |
|---|---|---|---|---|---|---|---|---|
| **Loom Size** | | **Needle Size** | | **Hook Size** | | **Yarn Weight** | | |
| Gauge | Peg C2C (in.) | US | mm | US | mm | US | UK/AU | Avg. sts/in |
| EFG | $\frac{3}{16}$ | 1-3 | 2.25-3.25mm | A-D | 2-3.125mm | 0-2 | 1-3 ply | 7-8 |
| FG | $\frac{1}{4}$ | 3-6 | 3.25-4mm | D-G | 3.125-4.25mm | 1-3 | 2,4 & 8-ply | 5-7 |
| SG | $\frac{5}{16}, \frac{3}{8}, \frac{7}{16}$ | 5-8 | 3.75-5mm | F-H | 3.75-5mm | 2-4 | 2,4 & 8-ply,DK | 4-5 |
| RG | $\frac{1}{2}, \frac{9}{16}$ | 8-10 | 5-6mm | H-J | 5-5.75mm | 4-5 | 8-12-ply/DK/Aran | 3-4 |
| LG | $\frac{5}{8}, \frac{11}{16}$ | 10-13 | 6-9mm | J-M | 5.75-9mm | 5-6 | 10-12-ply/Aran/Chunky | 2-3 |
| XLG | $\frac{3}{4}, \frac{13}{16}, \frac{7}{8}, \frac{15}{16}$ | 13-15 | 9-10mm | M-N+ | 9-10mm | 6-7 | 12-ply/Chunky | 1.5-3 |
| JUMBO | +/- $1\frac{1}{2}$ | 19-35 | 12.75-20+mm | M-Q+ | 9-30+mm | 6-7 | Chunky/Roving | .75-1 |

**EFG**: Extra Fine Gauge | **FG**: Fine Gauge | **SG**: Small Gauge |**RG**: Regular Gauge | **LG**: Large Gauge | **XLG**: Extra Large Gauge | **JUMBO**: Jumbo

# PROJECT PAGE

## PROJECT

Name: _____     Start Date: _____

Made for: _____     End Date: _____

## PATTERN

Pattern: _____

Source: _____
(Website / Book / Magazine)

Gauge: _____ sts X _____ rows in _____ in/cm

Size: _____

## YARN

| Name | Color | # Skeins /Yds |
|------|-------|---------------|
|      |       |               |
|      |       |               |
|      |       |               |
|      |       |               |

Attach Yarn Label(s) Here

## MATERIALS

### Needle/Hook/Loom

| Name/Brand/Style | Size |
|------------------|------|
|                  |      |
|                  |      |
|                  |      |
|                  |      |

### Other Materials

| | |
|---|---|
| ◯ tapestry needle | ◯ |
| ◯ stitch marker(s) _____ | ◯ |
| ◯ | ◯ |

Remove this page and keep it with your project for a quick reference.

Knit & Crochet Planner          goodknitkisses.com

## PROJECT NOTES

_____

_____

_____

_____

_____

_____

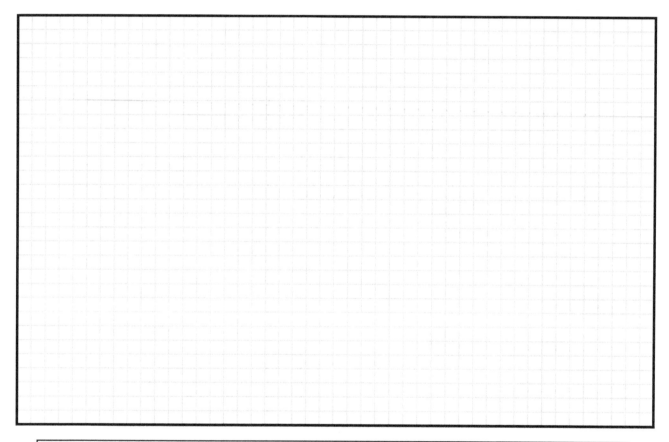

| Loom-Needle-Hook Equivalence Chart with Recommended Yarn Weight | | | | | | | | |
|---|---|---|---|---|---|---|---|---|
| Loom Size | | Needle Size | | Hook Size | | Yarn Weight | | |
| Gauge | Peg C2C (in.) | US | mm | US | mm | US | UK/AU | Avg. sts/in |
| EFG | ³⁄₁₆ | 1-3 | 2.25-3.25mm | A-D | 2-3.125mm | 0-2 | 1-3 ply | 7-8 |
| FG | ¼ | 3-6 | 3.25-4mm | D-G | 3.125-4.25mm | 1-3 | 2,4 & 8-ply | 5-7 |
| SG | ⁵⁄₁₆, ³⁄₈, ⁷⁄₁₆ | 5-8 | 3.75-5mm | F-H | 3.75-5mm | 2-4 | 2,4 & 8-ply,DK | 4-5 |
| RG | ½, ⁹⁄₁₆ | 8-10 | 5-6mm | H-J | 5-5.75mm | 4-5 | 8-12-ply/DK/Aran | 3-4 |
| LG | ⁵⁄₈, ¹¹⁄₁₆ | 10-13 | 6-9mm | J-M | 5.75-9mm | 5-6 | 10-12-ply/Aran/Chunky | 2-3 |
| XLG | ¾, ¹³⁄₁₆, ⁷⁄₈, ¹⁵⁄₁₆ | 13-15 | 9-10mm | M-N+ | 9-10mm | 6-7 | 12-ply/Chunky | 1.5-3 |
| JUMBO | +/- 1½ | 19-35 | 12.75-20+mm | M-Q+ | 9-30+mm | 6-7 | Chunky/Roving | .75-1 |

**EFG**: Extra Fine Gauge | **FG**: Fine Gauge | **SG**: Small Gauge |**RG**: Regular Gauge | **LG**: Large Gauge | **XLG**: Extra Large Gauge | **JUMBO**: Jumbo

Knit & Crochet Planner                    goodknitkisses.com

# PROJECT PAGE

## PROJECT

Name: _____     Start Date: _____

Made for: _____     End Date: _____

## PATTERN

Pattern: _____

Source: _____
(Website / Book / Magazine)

Gauge: _____ sts X _____ rows in _____ in/cm

Size: _____

## YARN

| Name | Color | # Skeins /Yds |
|------|-------|---------------|
|      |       |               |
|      |       |               |
|      |       |               |
|      |       |               |

Attach Yarn Label(s) Here

## MATERIALS

### Needle/Hook/Loom

| Name/Brand/Style | Size |
|------------------|------|
|                  |      |
|                  |      |
|                  |      |
|                  |      |

### Other Materials

| | |
|---|---|
| ◯ tapestry needle | ◯ |
| ◯ stitch marker(s) _____ | ◯ |
| ◯ | ◯ |

Remove this page and keep it with your project for a quick reference.

Knit & Crochet Planner              goodknitkisses.com

PROJECT

# PROJECT NOTES

_____

_____

_____

_____

_____

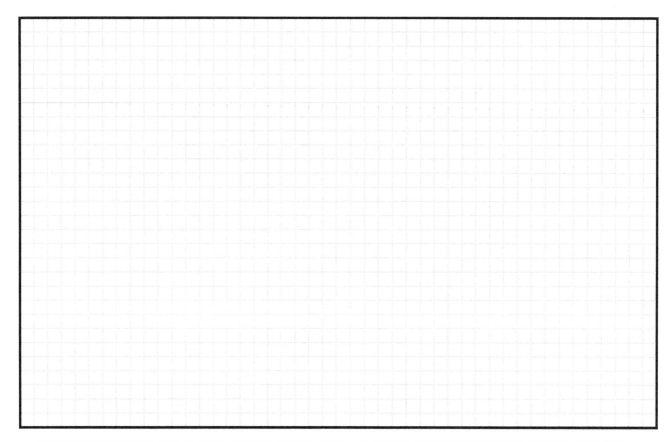

| Loom-Needle-Hook Equivalence Chart with Recommended Yarn Weight | | | | | | | | |
|---|---|---|---|---|---|---|---|---|
| Loom Size | | Needle Size | | Hook Size | | Yarn Weight | | |
| Gauge | Peg C2C (in.) | US | mm | US | mm | US | UK/AU | Avg. sts/in |
| EFG | $^3/_{16}$ | 1-3 | 2.25-3.25mm | A-D | 2-3.125mm | 0-2 | 1-3 ply | 7-8 |
| FG | $^1/_4$ | 3-6 | 3.25-4mm | D-G | 3.125-4.25mm | 1-3 | 2,4 & 8-ply | 5-7 |
| SG | $^5/_{16}$, $^3/_8$, $^7/_{16}$ | 5-8 | 3.75-5mm | F-H | 3.75-5mm | 2-4 | 2,4 & 8-ply, DK | 4-5 |
| RG | $^1/_2$, $^9/_{16}$ | 8-10 | 5-6mm | H-J | 5-5.75mm | 4-5 | 8-12-ply/DK/Aran | 3-4 |
| LG | $^5/_8$, $^{11}/_{16}$ | 10-13 | 6-9mm | J-M | 5.75-9mm | 5-6 | 10-12-ply/Aran/Chunky | 2-3 |
| XLG | $^3/_4$, $^{13}/_{16}$, $^7/_8$, $^{15}/_{16}$ | 13-15 | 9-10mm | M-N+ | 9-10mm | 6-7 | 12-ply/Chunky | 1.5-3 |
| JUMBO | +/- $1^1/_2$ | 19-35 | 12.75-20+mm | M-Q+ | 9-30+mm | 6-7 | Chunky/Roving | .75-1 |

**EFG**: Extra Fine Gauge | **FG**: Fine Gauge | **SG**: Small Gauge | **RG**: Regular Gauge | **LG**: Large Gauge | **XLG**: Extra Large Gauge | **JUMBO**: Jumbo

Knit & Crochet Planner  goodknitkisses.com

# PROJECT PAGE

## PROJECT

Name: _____    Start Date: _____

Made for: _____    End Date: _____

## PATTERN

Pattern: _____

Source: _____
(Website / Book / Magazine)

Gauge: _____ sts X _____ rows in _____ in/cm

Size: _____

## YARN

| Name | Color | # Skeins /Yds |
|------|-------|---------------|
|      |       |               |
|      |       |               |
|      |       |               |
|      |       |               |

Attach Yarn Label(s) Here

## MATERIALS

### Needle/Hook/Loom

| Name/Brand/Style | Size |
|------------------|------|
|                  |      |
|                  |      |
|                  |      |
|                  |      |

### Other Materials

| | |
|---|---|
| ◯ tapestry needle | ◯ |
| ◯ stitch marker(s) _____ | ◯ |
| ◯ | ◯ |

Remove this page and keep it with your project for a quick reference.

Knit & Crochet Planner                     goodknitkisses.com

## PROJECT NOTES

_____

_____

_____

_____

_____

_____

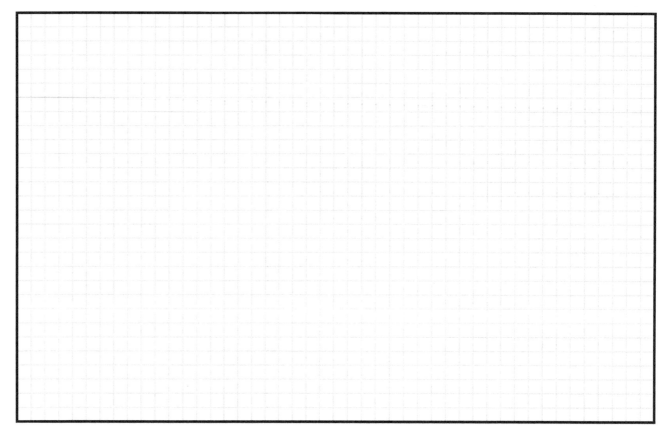

| Loom-Needle-Hook Equivalence Chart with Recommended Yarn Weight | | | | | | | | |
|---|---|---|---|---|---|---|---|---|
| Loom Size | | Needle Size | | Hook Size | | Yarn Weight | | |
| Gauge | Peg C2C (in.) | US | mm | US | mm | US | UK/AU | Avg. sts/in |
| EFG | $^3/_{16}$ | 1-3 | 2.25-3.25mm | A-D | 2-3.125mm | 0-2 | 1-3 ply | 7-8 |
| FG | $^1/_4$ | 3-6 | 3.25-4mm | D-G | 3.125-4.25mm | 1-3 | 2,4 & 8-ply | 5-7 |
| SG | $^5/_{16}$, $^3/_8$, $^7/_{16}$ | 5-8 | 3.75-5mm | F-H | 3.75-5mm | 2-4 | 2,4 & 8-ply,DK | 4-5 |
| RG | $^1/_2$, $^9/_{16}$ | 8-10 | 5-6mm | H-J | 5-5.75mm | 4-5 | 8-12-ply/DK/Aran | 3-4 |
| LG | $^5/_8$, $^{11}/_{16}$ | 10-13 | 6-9mm | J-M | 5.75-9mm | 5-6 | 10-12-ply/Aran/Chunky | 2-3 |
| XLG | $^3/_4$, $^{13}/_{16}$, $^7/_8$, $^{15}/_{16}$ | 13-15 | 9-10mm | M-N+ | 9-10mm | 6-7 | 12-ply/Chunky | 1.5-3 |
| JUMBO | +/- $1^1/_2$ | 19-35 | 12.75-20+mm | M-Q+ | 9-30+mm | 6-7 | Chunky/Roving | .75-1 |

**EFG**: Extra Fine Gauge | **FG**: Fine Gauge | **SG**: Small Gauge |**RG**: Regular Gauge | **LG**: Large Gauge | **XLG**: Extra Large Gauge | **JUMBO**: Jumbo

Knit & Crochet Planner        goodknitkisses.com

# PROJECT PAGE

## PROJECT

Name: _____          Start Date: _____

Made for: _____       End Date: _____

## PATTERN

Pattern: _____

Source: _____
(Website / Book / Magazine)

Gauge: _____ sts X _____ rows in _____ in/cm

Size: _____

## YARN

| Name | Color | # Skeins /Yds |
|------|-------|---------------|
|      |       |               |
|      |       |               |
|      |       |               |
|      |       |               |

Attach Yarn Label(s) Here

## MATERIALS

### Needle/Hook/Loom

| Name/Brand/Style | Size |
|------------------|------|
|                  |      |
|                  |      |
|                  |      |
|                  |      |

### Other Materials

| ◯ tapestry needle | ◯ |
| ◯ stitch marker(s) _____ | ◯ |
| ◯ | ◯ |

Remove this page and keep it with your project for a quick reference.

## PROJECT NOTES

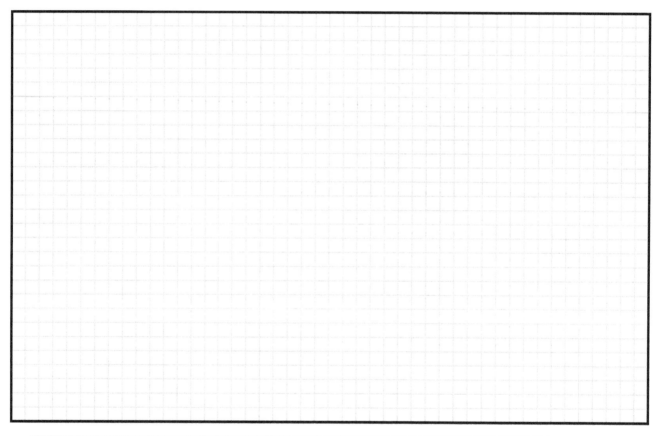

| Loom-Needle-Hook Equivalence Chart with Recommended Yarn Weight | | | | | | | | |
|---|---|---|---|---|---|---|---|---|
| Loom Size | | Needle Size | | Hook Size | | Yarn Weight | | |
| Gauge | Peg C2C (in.) | US | mm | US | mm | US | UK/AU | Avg. sts/in |
| EFG | ³⁄₁₆ | 1-3 | 2.25-3.25mm | A-D | 2-3.125mm | 0-2 | 1-3 ply | 7-8 |
| FG | ¹⁄₄ | 3-6 | 3.25-4mm | D-G | 3.125-4.25mm | 1-3 | 2,4 & 8-ply | 5-7 |
| SG | ⁵⁄₁₆, ³⁄₈, ⁷⁄₁₆ | 5-8 | 3.75-5mm | F-H | 3.75-5mm | 2-4 | 2,4 & 8-ply,DK | 4-5 |
| RG | ¹⁄₂, ⁹⁄₁₆ | 8-10 | 5-6mm | H-J | 5-5.75mm | 4-5 | 8-12-ply/DK/Aran | 3-4 |
| LG | ⁵⁄₈, ¹¹⁄₁₆ | 10-13 | 6-9mm | J-M | 5.75-9mm | 5-6 | 10-12-ply/Aran/Chunky | 2-3 |
| XLG | ³⁄₄, ¹³⁄₁₆, ⁷⁄₈, ¹⁵⁄₁₆ | 13-15 | 9-10mm | M-N+ | 9-10mm | 6-7 | 12-ply/Chunky | 1.5-3 |
| JUMBO | +/- 1½ | 19-35 | 12.75-20+mm | M-Q+ | 9-30+mm | 6-7 | Chunky/Roving | .75-1 |

**EFG**: Extra Fine Gauge | **FG**: Fine Gauge | **SG**: Small Gauge | **RG**: Regular Gauge | **LG**: Large Gauge | **XLG**: Extra Large Gauge | **JUMBO**: Jumbo

Knit & Crochet Planner

goodknitkisses.com

# PROJECT PAGE

## PROJECT

Name: ______________________ Start Date: ______________

Made for: ______________________ End Date: ______________

## PATTERN

Pattern: ______________________

Source: ______________________
(Website / Book / Magazine)

Gauge: ____ sts X ____ rows in ______ in/cm

Size: ______________________

## YARN

| Name | Color | # Skeins /Yds |
|---|---|---|
| | | |
| | | |
| | | |
| | | |

Attach Yarn Label(s) Here

## MATERIALS

Needle/Hook/Loom

| Name/Brand/Style | Size |
|---|---|
| | |
| | |
| | |
| | |

Other Materials

| | |
|---|---|
| ◯ tapestry needle | ◯ |
| ◯ stitch marker(s) _____ | ◯ |
| ◯ | ◯ |

Remove this page and keep it with your project for a quick reference.

## PROJECT NOTES

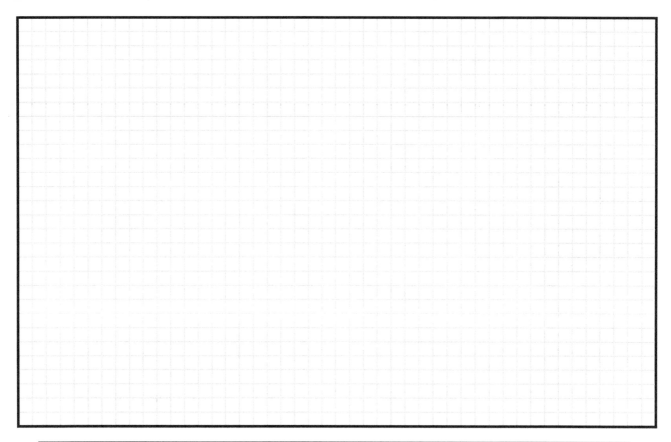

| Loom-Needle-Hook Equivalence Chart with Recommended Yarn Weight | | | | | | | |
|---|---|---|---|---|---|---|---|
| **Loom Size** | | **Needle Size** | | **Hook Size** | | **Yarn Weight** | |
| Gauge | Peg C2C (in.) | US | mm | US | mm | US | UK/AU | Avg. sts/in |
| EFG | $3/16$ | 1-3 | 2.25-3.25mm | A-D | 2-3.125mm | 0-2 | 1-3 ply | 7-8 |
| FG | $1/4$ | 3-6 | 3.25-4mm | D-G | 3.125-4.25mm | 1-3 | 2,4 & 8-ply | 5-7 |
| SG | $5/16, 3/8, 7/16$ | 5-8 | 3.75-5mm | F-H | 3.75-5mm | 2-4 | 2,4 & 8-ply,DK | 4-5 |
| RG | $1/2, 9/16$ | 8-10 | 5-6mm | H-J | 5-5.75mm | 4-5 | 8-12-ply/DK/Aran | 3-4 |
| LG | $5/8, 11/16$ | 10-13 | 6-9mm | J-M | 5.75-9mm | 5-6 | 10-12-ply/Aran/Chunky | 2-3 |
| XLG | $3/4, 13/16, 7/8, 15/16$ | 13-15 | 9-10mm | M-N+ | 9-10mm | 6-7 | 12-ply/Chunky | 1.5-3 |
| JUMBO | +/- $1\frac{1}{2}$ | 19-35 | 12.75-20+mm | M-Q+ | 9-30+mm | 6-7 | Chunky/Roving | .75-1 |

**EFG**: Extra Fine Gauge | **FG**: Fine Gauge | **SG**: Small Gauge |**RG**: Regular Gauge | **LG**: Large Gauge | **XLG**: Extra Large Gauge | **JUMBO**: Jumbo

Knit & Crochet Planner  goodknitkisses.com

# PROJECT PAGE

## PROJECT

Name: _____  Start Date: _____

Made for: _____  End Date: _____

## PATTERN

Pattern: _____

Source: _____
(Website / Book / Magazine)

Gauge: ____ sts X ____ rows in _____ in/cm

Size: _____

## YARN

| Name | Color | # Skeins /Yds |
|---|---|---|
|  |  |  |
|  |  |  |
|  |  |  |
|  |  |  |

Attach Yarn Label(s) Here

## MATERIALS

### Needle/Hook/Loom

| Name/Brand/Style | Size |
|---|---|
|  |  |
|  |  |
|  |  |
|  |  |

### Other Materials

| | |
|---|---|
| ○ tapestry needle | ○ |
| ○ stitch marker(s) _____ | ○ |
| ○ | ○ |

Remove this page and keep it with your project for a quick reference.

Knit & Crochet Planner          goodknitkisses.com

## PROJECT NOTES

_____

_____

_____

_____

_____

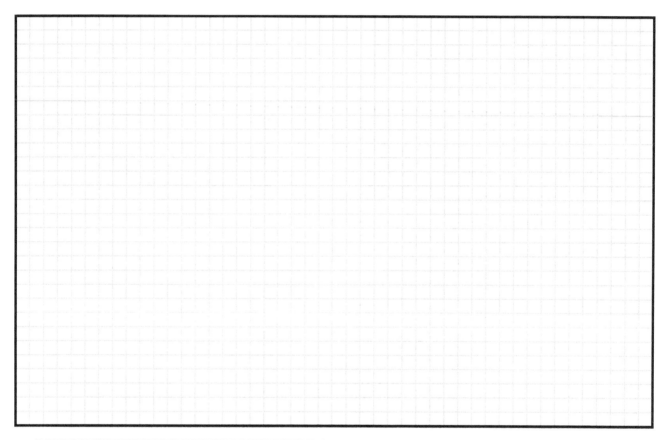

| Loom-Needle-Hook Equivalence Chart with Recommended Yarn Weight | | | | | | | | |
|---|---|---|---|---|---|---|---|---|
| Loom Size | | Needle Size | | Hook Size | | Yarn Weight | | |
| Gauge | Peg C2C (in.) | US | mm | US | mm | US | UK/AU | Avg. sts/in |
| EFG | $^3/_{16}$ | 1-3 | 2.25-3.25mm | A-D | 2-3.125mm | 0-2 | 1-3 ply | 7-8 |
| FG | $^1/_4$ | 3-6 | 3.25-4mm | D-G | 3.125-4.25mm | 1-3 | 2,4 & 8-ply | 5-7 |
| SG | $^5/_{16}, ^3/_8, ^7/_{16}$ | 5-8 | 3.75-5mm | F-H | 3.75-5mm | 2-4 | 2,4 & 8-ply,DK | 4-5 |
| RG | $^1/_2, ^9/_{16}$ | 8-10 | 5-6mm | H-J | 5-5.75mm | 4-5 | 8-12-ply/DK/Aran | 3-4 |
| LG | $^5/_8, ^{11}/_{16}$ | 10-13 | 6-9mm | J-M | 5.75-9mm | 5-6 | 10-12-ply/Aran/Chunky | 2-3 |
| XLG | $^3/_4, ^{13}/_{16}, ^7/_8, ^{15}/_{16}$ | 13-15 | 9-10mm | M-N+ | 9-10mm | 6-7 | 12-ply/Chunky | 1.5-3 |
| JUMBO | +/- $1^1/_2$ | 19-35 | 12.75-20+mm | M-Q+ | 9-30+mm | 6-7 | Chunky/Roving | .75-1 |

**EFG**: Extra Fine Gauge | **FG**: Fine Gauge | **SG**: Small Gauge | **RG**: Regular Gauge | **LG**: Large Gauge | **XLG**: Extra Large Gauge | **JUMBO**: Jumbo

Knit & Crochet Planner                    goodknitkisses.com

# PROJECT PAGE

## PROJECT

Name: _____     Start Date: _____

Made for: _____     End Date: _____

## PATTERN

Pattern: _____

Source: _____
(Website / Book / Magazine)

Gauge: _____ sts X _____ rows in _____ in/cm

Size: _____

## YARN

| Name | Color | # Skeins /Yds |
|------|-------|---------------|
|      |       |               |
|      |       |               |
|      |       |               |
|      |       |               |

Attach Yarn Label(s) Here

## MATERIALS

### Needle/Hook/Loom

| Name/Brand/Style | Size |
|------------------|------|
|                  |      |
|                  |      |
|                  |      |
|                  |      |

### Other Materials

| | |
|---|---|
| ⚪ tapestry needle | ⚪ |
| ⚪ stitch marker(s) _____ | ⚪ |
| ⚪ | ⚪ |

Remove this page and keep it with your project for a quick reference.

Knit & Crochet Planner                    goodknitkisses.com

# PROJECT NOTES

_____

_____

_____

_____

_____

_____

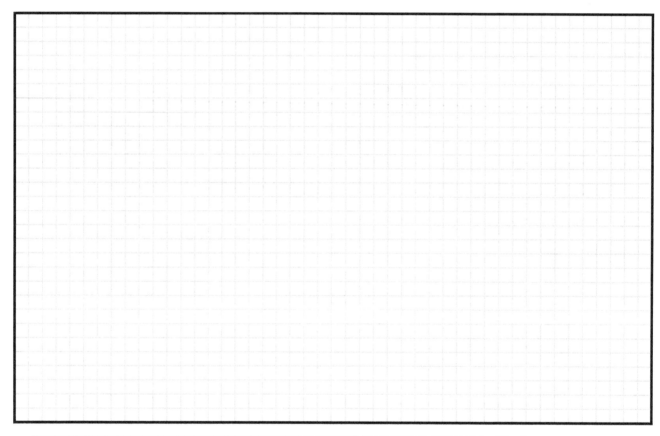

| Loom-Needle-Hook Equivalence Chart with Recommended Yarn Weight | | | | | | | | |
|---|---|---|---|---|---|---|---|---|
| Loom Size | | Needle Size | | Hook Size | | Yarn Weight | | |
| Gauge | Peg C2C (in.) | US | mm | US | mm | US | UK/AU | Avg. sts/in |
| EFG | $3/16$ | 1-3 | 2.25-3.25mm | A-D | 2-3.125mm | 0-2 | 1-3 ply | 7-8 |
| FG | $1/4$ | 3-6 | 3.25-4mm | D-G | 3.125-4.25mm | 1-3 | 2,4 & 8-ply | 5-7 |
| SG | $5/16$, $3/8$, $7/16$ | 5-8 | 3.75-5mm | F-H | 3.75-5mm | 2-4 | 2,4 & 8-ply,DK | 4-5 |
| RG | $1/2$, $9/16$ | 8-10 | 5-6mm | H-J | 5-5.75mm | 4-5 | 8-12-ply/DK/Aran | 3-4 |
| LG | $5/8$, $11/16$ | 10-13 | 6-9mm | J-M | 5.75-9mm | 5-6 | 10-12-ply/Aran/Chunky | 2-3 |
| XLG | $3/4$, $13/16$, $7/8$, $15/16$ | 13-15 | 9-10mm | M-N+ | 9-10mm | 6-7 | 12-ply/Chunky | 1.5-3 |
| JUMBO | +/- $1 1/2$ | 19-35 | 12.75-20+mm | M-Q+ | 9-30+mm | 6-7 | Chunky/Roving | .75-1 |

**EFG**: Extra Fine Gauge | **FG**: Fine Gauge | **SG**: Small Gauge | **RG**: Regular Gauge | **LG**: Large Gauge | **XLG**: Extra Large Gauge | **JUMBO**: Jumbo

Knit & Crochet Planner  goodknitkisses.com

# PROJECT PAGE

## PROJECT

Name: _____        Start Date: _____

Made for: _____    End Date: _____

## PATTERN

Pattern: _____

Source: _____
(Website / Book / Magazine)

Gauge: ____ sts X ____ rows in _____ in/cm

Size: _____

## MATERIALS

### Needle/Hook/Loom

| Name/Brand/Style | Size |
|---|---|
|  |  |
|  |  |
|  |  |
|  |  |

### Other Materials

| | |
|---|---|
| ◯ tapestry needle | ◯ |
| ◯ stitch marker(s) _____ | ◯ |
| ◯ | ◯ |

## YARN

| Name | Color | # Skeins /Yds |
|---|---|---|
|  |  |  |
|  |  |  |
|  |  |  |
|  |  |  |

Attach Yarn Label(s) Here

Remove this page and keep it with your project for a quick reference.

Knit & Crochet Planner        goodknitkisses.com

## PROJECT NOTES

_____

_____

_____

_____

_____

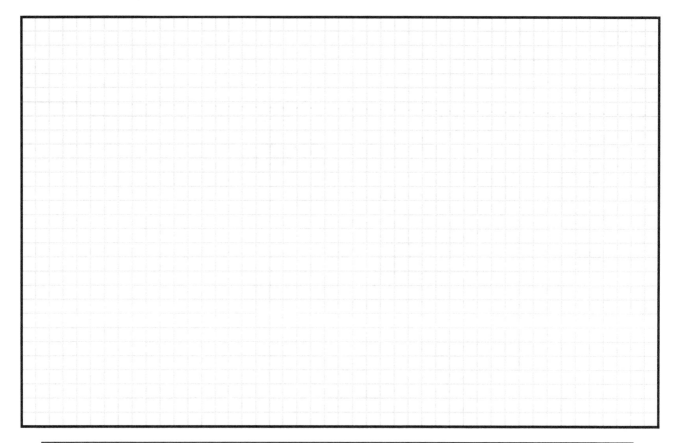

| Loom-Needle-Hook Equivalence Chart with Recommended Yarn Weight | | | | | | | | |
|---|---|---|---|---|---|---|---|---|
| Loom Size | | Needle Size | | Hook Size | | Yarn Weight | | |
| Gauge | Peg C2C (in.) | US | mm | US | mm | US | UK/AU | Avg. sts/in |
| EFG | $^{3}/_{16}$ | 1-3 | 2.25-3.25mm | A-D | 2-3.125mm | 0-2 | 1-3 ply | 7-8 |
| FG | $^{1}/_{4}$ | 3-6 | 3.25-4mm | D-G | 3.125-4.25mm | 1-3 | 2,4 & 8-ply | 5-7 |
| SG | $^{5}/_{16}$, $^{3}/_{8}$, $^{7}/_{16}$ | 5-8 | 3.75-5mm | F-H | 3.75-5mm | 2-4 | 2,4 & 8-ply,DK | 4-5 |
| RG | $^{1}/_{2}$, $^{9}/_{16}$ | 8-10 | 5-6mm | H-J | 5-5.75mm | 4-5 | 8-12-ply/DK/Aran | 3-4 |
| LG | $^{5}/_{8}$, $^{11}/_{16}$ | 10-13 | 6-9mm | J-M | 5.75-9mm | 5-6 | 10-12-ply/Aran/Chunky | 2-3 |
| XLG | $^{3}/_{4}$, $^{13}/_{16}$, $^{7}/_{8}$, $^{15}/_{16}$ | 13-15 | 9-10mm | M-N+ | 9-10mm | 6-7 | 12-ply/Chunky | 1.5-3 |
| JUMBO | +/- $1^{1}/_{2}$ | 19-35 | 12.75-20+mm | M-Q+ | 9-30+mm | 6-7 | Chunky/Roving | .75-1 |

**EFG**: Extra Fine Gauge | **FG**: Fine Gauge | **SG**: Small Gauge |**RG**: Regular Gauge | **LG**: Large Gauge | **XLG**: Extra Large Gauge | **JUMBO**: Jumbo

Knit & Crochet Planner  goodknitkisses.com

# PROJECT PAGE

PROJECT

## PROJECT

Name: ______________________ Start Date: ______________

Made for: ______________________ End Date: ______________

## PATTERN

Pattern: ______________________

Source: ______________________
(Website / Book / Magazine)

Gauge: ____ sts X ____ rows in ______ in/cm

Size: ______________________

## YARN

| Name | Color | # Skeins /Yds |
|---|---|---|
| | | |
| | | |
| | | |
| | | |

Attach Yarn Label(s) Here

## MATERIALS

Needle/Hook/Loom

| Name/Brand/Style | Size |
|---|---|
| | |
| | |
| | |
| | |

Other Materials

| | |
|---|---|
| ◯ tapestry needle | ◯ |
| ◯ stitch marker(s) _____ | ◯ |
| ◯ | ◯ |

Remove this page and keep it with your project for a quick reference.

PROJECT

## PROJECT NOTES

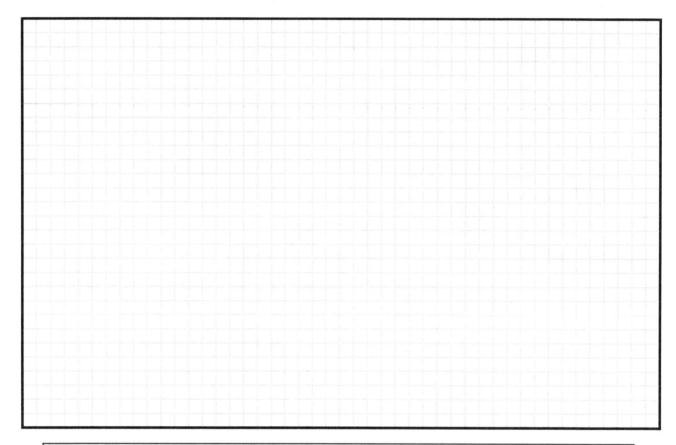

| Loom-Needle-Hook Equivalence Chart with Recommended Yarn Weight | | | | | | | | |
|---|---|---|---|---|---|---|---|---|
| Loom Size | | Needle Size | | Hook Size | | Yarn Weight | | |
| Gauge | Peg C2C (in.) | US | mm | US | mm | US | UK/AU | Avg. sts/in |
| EFG | 3/16 | 1-3 | 2.25-3.25mm | A-D | 2-3.125mm | 0-2 | 1-3 ply | 7-8 |
| FG | 1/4 | 3-6 | 3.25-4mm | D-G | 3.125-4.25mm | 1-3 | 2,4 & 8-ply | 5-7 |
| SG | 5/16, 3/8, 7/16 | 5-8 | 3.75-5mm | F-H | 3.75-5mm | 2-4 | 2,4 & 8-ply,DK | 4-5 |
| RG | 1/2, 9/16 | 8-10 | 5-6mm | H-J | 5-5.75mm | 4-5 | 8-12-ply/DK/Aran | 3-4 |
| LG | 5/8, 11/16 | 10-13 | 6-9mm | J-M | 5.75-9mm | 5-6 | 10-12-ply/Aran/Chunky | 2-3 |
| XLG | 3/4, 13/16, 7/8, 15/16 | 13-15 | 9-10mm | M-N+ | 9-10mm | 6-7 | 12-ply/Chunky | 1.5-3 |
| JUMBO | +/- 1 1/2 | 19-35 | 12.75-20+mm | M-Q+ | 9-30+mm | 6-7 | Chunky/Roving | .75-1 |

**EFG**: Extra Fine Gauge | **FG**: Fine Gauge | **SG**: Small Gauge |**RG**: Regular Gauge | **LG**: Large Gauge | **XLG**: Extra Large Gauge | **JUMBO**: Jumbo

Knit & Crochet Planner          goodknitkisses.com

# PROJECT PAGE

PROJECT

## PROJECT

Name: _____   Start Date: _____

Made for: _____   End Date: _____

## PATTERN

Pattern: _____

Source: _____
                (Website / Book / Magazine)

Gauge: ____ sts X ____ rows in _____ in/cm

Size: _____

## YARN

| Name | Color | # Skeins /Yds |
|------|-------|---------------|
|      |       |               |
|      |       |               |
|      |       |               |
|      |       |               |

Attach Yarn Label(s) Here

## MATERIALS

### Needle/Hook/Loom

| Name/Brand/Style | Size |
|------------------|------|
|                  |      |
|                  |      |
|                  |      |
|                  |      |

### Other Materials

| | |
|---|---|
| ◯ tapestry needle | ◯ |
| ◯ stitch marker(s) _____ | ◯ |
| ◯ | ◯ |

Remove this page and keep it with your project for a quick reference.

Knit & Crochet Planner          goodknitkisses.com

# PROJECT NOTES

_____

_____

_____

_____

_____

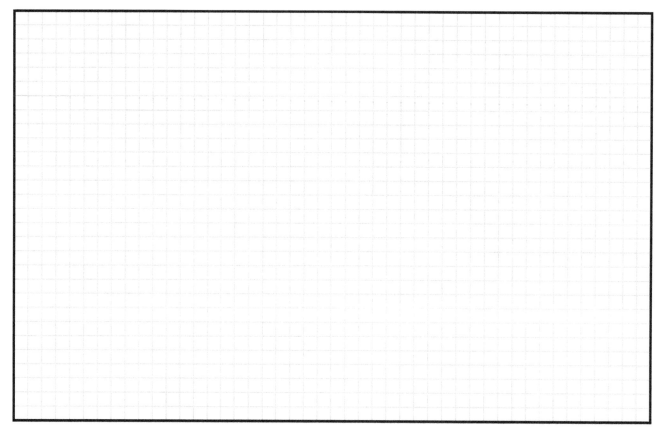

| Loom-Needle-Hook Equivalence Chart with Recommended Yarn Weight | | | | | | | | |
|---|---|---|---|---|---|---|---|---|
| Loom Size | | Needle Size | | Hook Size | | Yarn Weight | | |
| Gauge | Peg C2C (in.) | US | mm | US | mm | US | UK/AU | Avg. sts/in |
| EFG | ³/₁₆ | 1-3 | 2.25-3.25mm | A-D | 2-3.125mm | 0-2 | 1-3 ply | 7-8 |
| FG | ¹/₄ | 3-6 | 3.25-4mm | D-G | 3.125-4.25mm | 1-3 | 2,4 & 8-ply | 5-7 |
| SG | ⁵/₁₆, ³/₈, ⁷/₁₆ | 5-8 | 3.75-5mm | F-H | 3.75-5mm | 2-4 | 2,4 & 8-ply,DK | 4-5 |
| RG | ¹/₂, ⁹/₁₆ | 8-10 | 5-6mm | H-J | 5-5.75mm | 4-5 | 8-12-ply/DK/Aran | 3-4 |
| LG | ⁵/₈, ¹¹/₁₆ | 10-13 | 6-9mm | J-M | 5.75-9mm | 5-6 | 10-12-ply/Aran/Chunky | 2-3 |
| XLG | ³/₄, ¹³/₁₆, ⁷/₈, ¹⁵/₁₆ | 13-15 | 9-10mm | M-N+ | 9-10mm | 6-7 | 12-ply/Chunky | 1.5-3 |
| JUMBO | +/- 1¹/₂ | 19-35 | 12.75-20+mm | M-Q+ | 9-30+mm | 6-7 | Chunky/Roving | .75-1 |

**EFG**: Extra Fine Gauge | **FG**: Fine Gauge | **SG**: Small Gauge |**RG**: Regular Gauge | **LG**: Large Gauge | **XLG**: Extra Large Gauge | **JUMBO**: Jumbo

# PROJECT PAGE

## PROJECT

Name: _____    Start Date: _____

Made for: _____    End Date: _____

## PATTERN

Pattern: _____

Source: _____
(Website / Book / Magazine)

Gauge: _____ sts X _____ rows in _____ in/cm

Size: _____

## YARN

| Name | Color | # Skeins /Yds |
|------|-------|---------------|
|      |       |               |
|      |       |               |
|      |       |               |
|      |       |               |

Attach Yarn Label(s) Here

## MATERIALS

### Needle/Hook/Loom

| Name/Brand/Style | Size |
|------------------|------|
|                  |      |
|                  |      |
|                  |      |
|                  |      |

### Other Materials

| | |
|---|---|
| ◯ tapestry needle | ◯ |
| ◯ stitch marker(s) _____ | ◯ |
| ◯ | ◯ |

Remove this page and keep it with your project for a quick reference.

Knit & Crochet Planner          goodknitkisses.com

## PROJECT NOTES

_____

_____

_____

_____

_____

_____

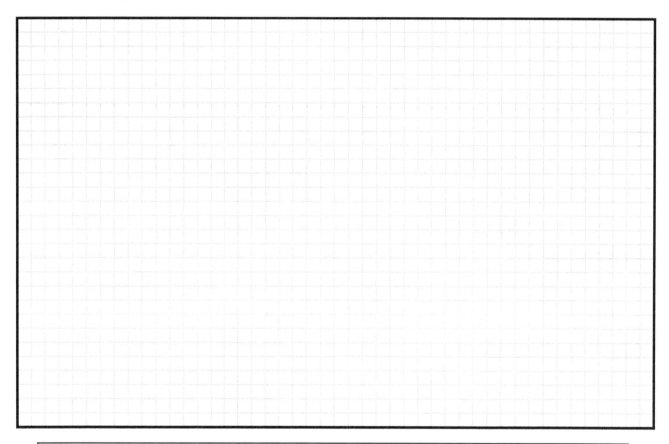

| Loom-Needle-Hook Equivalence Chart with Recommended Yarn Weight | | | | | | | | |
|---|---|---|---|---|---|---|---|---|
| Loom Size | | Needle Size | | Hook Size | | Yarn Weight | | |
| Gauge | Peg C2C (in.) | US | mm | US | mm | US | UK/AU | Avg. sts/in |
| EFG | 3/16 | 1-3 | 2.25-3.25mm | A-D | 2-3.125mm | 0-2 | 1-3 ply | 7-8 |
| FG | 1/4 | 3-6 | 3.25-4mm | D-G | 3.125-4.25mm | 1-3 | 2,4 & 8-ply | 5-7 |
| SG | 5/16, 3/8, 7/16 | 5-8 | 3.75-5mm | F-H | 3.75-5mm | 2-4 | 2,4 & 8-ply,DK | 4-5 |
| RG | 1/2, 9/16 | 8-10 | 5-6mm | H-J | 5-5.75mm | 4-5 | 8-12-ply/DK/Aran | 3-4 |
| LG | 5/8, 11/16 | 10-13 | 6-9mm | J-M | 5.75-9mm | 5-6 | 10-12-ply/Aran/Chunky | 2-3 |
| XLG | 3/4, 13/16, 7/8, 15/16 | 13-15 | 9-10mm | M-N+ | 9-10mm | 6-7 | 12-ply/Chunky | 1.5-3 |
| JUMBO | +/- 1 1/2 | 19-35 | 12.75-20+mm | M-Q+ | 9-30+mm | 6-7 | Chunky/Roving | .75-1 |

**EFG**: Extra Fine Gauge | **FG**: Fine Gauge | **SG**: Small Gauge |**RG**: Regular Gauge | **LG**: Large Gauge | **XLG**: Extra Large Gauge | **JUMBO**: Jumbo

# PROJECT PAGE

## PROJECT

Name: _____     Start Date: _____

Made for: _____     End Date: _____

## PATTERN

Pattern: _____

Source: _____
(Website / Book / Magazine)

Gauge: ____ sts X ____ rows in _____ in/cm

Size: _____

## MATERIALS

### Needle/Hook/Loom

| Name/Brand/Style | Size |
|---|---|
| | |
| | |
| | |
| | |

### Other Materials

| | |
|---|---|
| ◯ tapestry needle | ◯ |
| ◯ stitch marker(s) _____ | ◯ |
| ◯ | ◯ |

## YARN

| Name | Color | # Skeins /Yds |
|---|---|---|
| | | |
| | | |
| | | |
| | | |

Attach Yarn Label(s) Here

Remove this page and keep it with your project for a quick reference.

Knit & Crochet Planner                    goodknitkisses.com

PROJECT

# PROJECT NOTES

_____

_____

_____

_____

_____

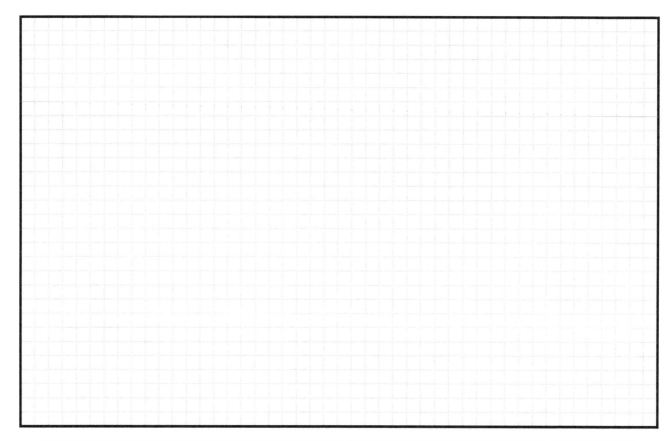

| Loom-Needle-Hook Equivalence Chart with Recommended Yarn Weight | | | | | | | | |
|---|---|---|---|---|---|---|---|---|
| Loom Size | | Needle Size | | Hook Size | | Yarn Weight | | |
| Gauge | Peg C2C (in.) | US | mm | US | mm | US | UK/AU | Avg. sts/in |
| EFG | $^3/_{16}$ | 1-3 | 2.25-3.25mm | A-D | 2-3.125mm | 0-2 | 1-3 ply | 7-8 |
| FG | $^1/_4$ | 3-6 | 3.25-4mm | D-G | 3.125-4.25mm | 1-3 | 2,4 & 8-ply | 5-7 |
| SG | $^5/_{16}, ^3/_8, ^7/_{16}$ | 5-8 | 3.75-5mm | F-H | 3.75-5mm | 2-4 | 2,4 & 8-ply,DK | 4-5 |
| RG | $^1/_2, ^9/_{16}$ | 8-10 | 5-6mm | H-J | 5-5.75mm | 4-5 | 8-12-ply/DK/Aran | 3-4 |
| LG | $^5/_8, ^{11}/_{16}$ | 10-13 | 6-9mm | J-M | 5.75-9mm | 5-6 | 10-12-ply/Aran/Chunky | 2-3 |
| XLG | $^3/_4, ^{13}/_{16}, ^7/_8, ^{15}/_{16}$ | 13-15 | 9-10mm | M-N+ | 9-10mm | 6-7 | 12-ply/Chunky | 1.5-3 |
| JUMBO | +/- $1^1/_2$ | 19-35 | 12.75-20+mm | M-Q+ | 9-30+mm | 6-7 | Chunky/Roving | .75-1 |

**EFG**: Extra Fine Gauge | **FG**: Fine Gauge | **SG**: Small Gauge | **RG**: Regular Gauge | **LG**: Large Gauge | **XLG**: Extra Large Gauge | **JUMBO**: Jumbo

Knit & Crochet Planner          goodknitkisses.com

# PROJECT PAGE

## PROJECT

Name: _____     Start Date: _____

Made for: _____     End Date: _____

## PATTERN

Pattern: _____

Source: _____
(Website / Book / Magazine)

Gauge: _____ sts X _____ rows in _____ in/cm

Size: _____

## YARN

| Name | Color | # Skeins /Yds |
|------|-------|---------------|
|      |       |               |
|      |       |               |
|      |       |               |
|      |       |               |

Attach Yarn Label(s) Here

## MATERIALS

### Needle/Hook/Loom

| Name/Brand/Style | Size |
|------------------|------|
|                  |      |
|                  |      |
|                  |      |
|                  |      |

### Other Materials

| | |
|---|---|
| ○ tapestry needle | ○ |
| ○ stitch marker(s) _____ | ○ |
| ○ | ○ |

Remove this page and keep it with your project for a quick reference.

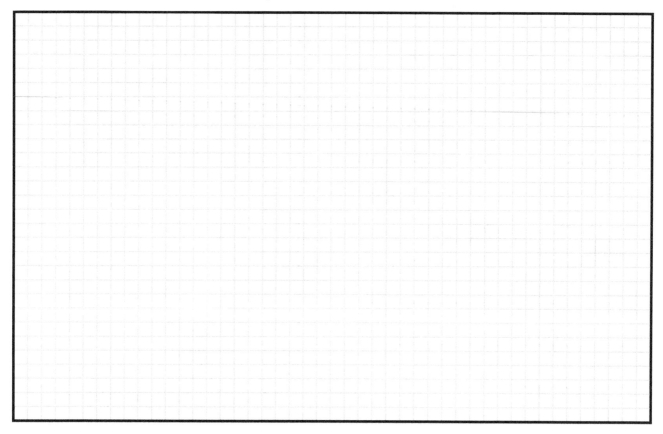

# PROJECT NOTES

PROJECT

_____

_____

_____

_____

_____

| Loom-Needle-Hook Equivalence Chart with Recommended Yarn Weight | | | | | | | | | |
|---|---|---|---|---|---|---|---|---|---|
| Loom Size | | Needle Size | | Hook Size | | Yarn Weight | | | |
| Gauge | Peg C2C (in.) | US | mm | US | mm | US | UK/AU | Avg. sts/in |
| EFG | ³⁄₁₆ | 1-3 | 2.25-3.25mm | A-D | 2-3.125mm | 0-2 | 1-3 ply | 7-8 |
| FG | ¹⁄₄ | 3-6 | 3.25-4mm | D-G | 3.125-4.25mm | 1-3 | 2,4 & 8-ply | 5-7 |
| SG | ⁵⁄₁₆, ³⁄₈, ⁷⁄₁₆ | 5-8 | 3.75-5mm | F-H | 3.75-5mm | 2-4 | 2,4 & 8-ply, DK | 4-5 |
| RG | ¹⁄₂, ⁹⁄₁₆ | 8-10 | 5-6mm | H-J | 5-5.75mm | 4-5 | 8-12-ply/DK/Aran | 3-4 |
| LG | ⁵⁄₈, ¹¹⁄₁₆ | 10-13 | 6-9mm | J-M | 5.75-9mm | 5-6 | 10-12-ply/Aran/Chunky | 2-3 |
| XLG | ³⁄₄, ¹³⁄₁₆, ⁷⁄₈, ¹⁵⁄₁₆ | 13-15 | 9-10mm | M-N+ | 9-10mm | 6-7 | 12-ply/Chunky | 1.5-3 |
| JUMBO | +/- 1¹⁄₂ | 19-35 | 12.75-20+mm | M-Q+ | 9-30+mm | 6-7 | Chunky/Roving | .75-1 |

**EFG**: Extra Fine Gauge | **FG**: Fine Gauge | **SG**: Small Gauge | **RG**: Regular Gauge | **LG**: Large Gauge | **XLG**: Extra Large Gauge | **JUMBO**: Jumbo

Knit & Crochet Planner              goodknitkisses.com

# PROJECT PAGE

## PROJECT

Name: _____     Start Date: _____

Made for: _____     End Date: _____

## PATTERN

Pattern: _____

Source: _____
(Website / Book / Magazine)

Gauge: ____ sts X ____ rows in _____ in/cm

Size: _____

## YARN

| Name | Color | # Skeins /Yds |
|------|-------|---------------|
|      |       |               |
|      |       |               |
|      |       |               |
|      |       |               |

Attach Yarn Label(s) Here

## MATERIALS

### Needle/Hook/Loom

| Name/Brand/Style | Size |
|------------------|------|
|                  |      |
|                  |      |
|                  |      |
|                  |      |

### Other Materials

| | |
|---|---|
| ○ tapestry needle | ○ |
| ○ stitch marker(s) _____ | ○ |
| ○ | ○ |

Remove this page and keep it with your project for a quick reference.

Knit & Crochet Planner  goodknitkisses.com

# PROJECT NOTES

_____

_____

_____

_____

_____

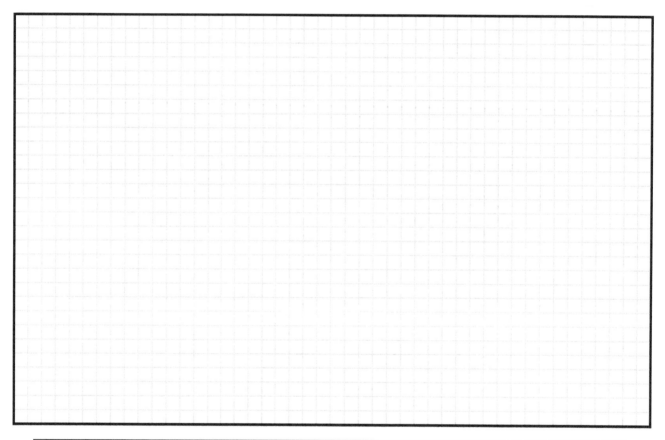

| Loom-Needle-Hook Equivalence Chart with Recommended Yarn Weight | | | | | | | | |
|---|---|---|---|---|---|---|---|---|
| Loom Size | | Needle Size | | Hook Size | | Yarn Weight | | |
| Gauge | Peg C2C (in.) | US | mm | US | mm | US | UK/AU | Avg. sts/in |
| EFG | $^3/_{16}$ | 1-3 | 2.25-3.25mm | A-D | 2-3.125mm | 0-2 | 1-3 ply | 7-8 |
| FG | $^1/_4$ | 3-6 | 3.25-4mm | D-G | 3.125-4.25mm | 1-3 | 2,4 & 8-ply | 5-7 |
| SG | $^5/_{16}$, $^3/_8$, $^7/_{16}$ | 5-8 | 3.75-5mm | F-H | 3.75-5mm | 2-4 | 2,4 & 8-ply,DK | 4-5 |
| RG | $^1/_2$, $^9/_{16}$ | 8-10 | 5-6mm | H-J | 5-5.75mm | 4-5 | 8-12-ply/DK/Aran | 3-4 |
| LG | $^5/_8$, $^{11}/_{16}$ | 10-13 | 6-9mm | J-M | 5.75-9mm | 5-6 | 10-12-ply/Aran/Chunky | 2-3 |
| XLG | $^3/_4$, $^{13}/_{16}$, $^7/_8$, $^{15}/_{16}$ | 13-15 | 9-10mm | M-N+ | 9-10mm | 6-7 | 12-ply/Chunky | 1.5-3 |
| JUMBO | +/- $1^1/_2$ | 19-35 | 12.75-20+mm | M-Q+ | 9-30+mm | 6-7 | Chunky/Roving | .75-1 |

**EFG**: Extra Fine Gauge | **FG**: Fine Gauge | **SG**: Small Gauge |**RG**: Regular Gauge | **LG**: Large Gauge | **XLG**: Extra Large Gauge | **JUMBO**: Jumbo

Knit & Crochet Planner          goodknitkisses.com

# PROJECT PAGE

## PROJECT

Name: _____    Start Date: _____

Made for: _____    End Date: _____

## PATTERN

Pattern: _____

Source: _____
(Website / Book / Magazine)

Gauge: ____ sts X ____ rows in _____ in/cm

Size: _____

## YARN

| Name | Color | # Skeins /Yds |
|------|-------|---------------|
|      |       |               |
|      |       |               |
|      |       |               |
|      |       |               |

Attach Yarn Label(s) Here

## MATERIALS

### Needle/Hook/Loom

| Name/Brand/Style | Size |
|------------------|------|
|                  |      |
|                  |      |
|                  |      |
|                  |      |

### Other Materials

| | |
|---|---|
| ○ tapestry needle | ○ |
| ○ stitch marker(s) _____ | ○ |
| ○ | ○ |

Remove this page and keep it with your project for a quick reference.

Knit & Crochet Planner        goodknitkisses.com

PROJECT

## PROJECT NOTES

_____

_____

_____

_____

_____

_____

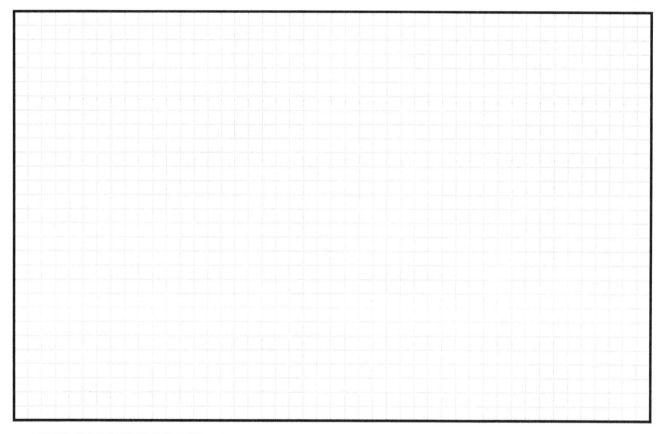

| Loom-Needle-Hook Equivalence Chart with Recommended Yarn Weight | | | | | | | | |
|---|---|---|---|---|---|---|---|---|
| Loom Size | | Needle Size | | Hook Size | | Yarn Weight | | |
| Gauge | Peg C2C (in.) | US | mm | US | mm | US | UK/AU | Avg. sts/in |
| EFG | 3/16 | 1-3 | 2.25-3.25mm | A-D | 2-3.125mm | 0-2 | 1-3 ply | 7-8 |
| FG | 1/4 | 3-6 | 3.25-4mm | D-G | 3.125-4.25mm | 1-3 | 2,4 & 8-ply | 5-7 |
| SG | 5/16, 3/8, 7/16 | 5-8 | 3.75-5mm | F-H | 3.75-5mm | 2-4 | 2,4 & 8-ply,DK | 4-5 |
| RG | 1/2, 9/16 | 8-10 | 5-6mm | H-J | 5-5.75mm | 4-5 | 8-12-ply/DK/Aran | 3-4 |
| LG | 5/8, 11/16 | 10-13 | 6-9mm | J-M | 5.75-9mm | 5-6 | 10-12-ply/Aran/Chunky | 2-3 |
| XLG | 3/4, 13/16, 7/8, 15/16 | 13-15 | 9-10mm | M-N+ | 9-10mm | 6-7 | 12-ply/Chunky | 1.5-3 |
| JUMBO | +/- 1 1/2 | 19-35 | 12.75-20+mm | M-Q+ | 9-30+mm | 6-7 | Chunky/Roving | .75-1 |

**EFG**: Extra Fine Gauge | **FG**: Fine Gauge | **SG**: Small Gauge |**RG**: Regular Gauge | **LG**: Large Gauge | **XLG**: Extra Large Gauge | **JUMBO**: Jumbo

Knit & Crochet Planner              goodknitkisses.com

# PROJECT PAGE

**PROJECT**

Name: _____     Start Date: _____

Made for: _____     End Date: _____

**PROJECT**

---

### PATTERN

Pattern: _____

Source: _____
              (Website / Book / Magazine)

Gauge: _____ sts X _____ rows in _____ in/cm

Size: _____

---

### YARN

| Name | Color | # Skeins /Yds |
|---|---|---|
|  |  |  |
|  |  |  |
|  |  |  |
|  |  |  |

Attach Yarn Label(s) Here

---

### MATERIALS

Needle/Hook/Loom

| Name/Brand/Style | Size |
|---|---|
|  |  |
|  |  |
|  |  |
|  |  |

Other Materials

| | |
|---|---|
| ○ tapestry needle | ○ |
| ○ stitch marker(s) _____ | ○ |
| ○ | ○ |

---

Remove this page and keep it with your project for a quick reference.

Knit & Crochet Planner          goodknitkisses.com

# PROJECT NOTES

_____

_____

_____

_____

_____

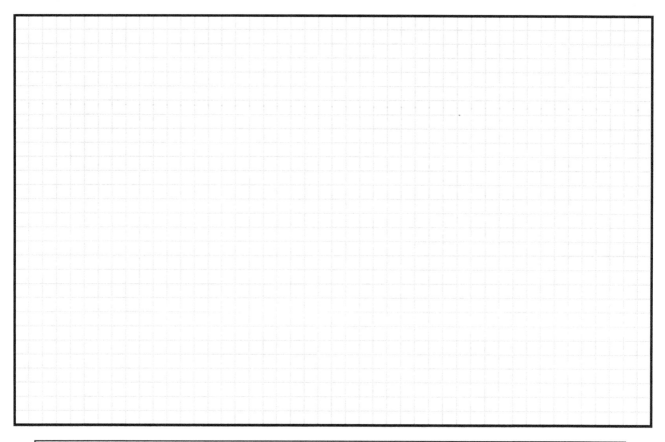

| Loom-Needle-Hook Equivalence Chart with Recommended Yarn Weight | | | | | | | | |
|---|---|---|---|---|---|---|---|---|
| Loom Size | | Needle Size | | Hook Size | | Yarn Weight | | |
| Gauge | Peg C2C (in.) | US | mm | US | mm | US | UK/AU | Avg. sts/in |
| EFG | $^3/_{16}$ | 1-3 | 2.25-3.25mm | A-D | 2-3.125mm | 0-2 | 1-3 ply | 7-8 |
| FG | $^1/_4$ | 3-6 | 3.25-4mm | D-G | 3.125-4.25mm | 1-3 | 2,4 & 8-ply | 5-7 |
| SG | $^5/_{16}$, $^3/_8$, $^7/_{16}$ | 5-8 | 3.75-5mm | F-H | 3.75-5mm | 2-4 | 2,4 & 8-ply,DK | 4-5 |
| RG | $^1/_2$, $^9/_{16}$ | 8-10 | 5-6mm | H-J | 5-5.75mm | 4-5 | 8-12-ply/DK/Aran | 3-4 |
| LG | $^5/_8$, $^{11}/_{16}$ | 10-13 | 6-9mm | J-M | 5.75-9mm | 5-6 | 10-12-ply/Aran/Chunky | 2-3 |
| XLG | $^3/_4$, $^{13}/_{16}$, $^7/_8$, $^{15}/_{16}$ | 13-15 | 9-10mm | M-N+ | 9-10mm | 6-7 | 12-ply/Chunky | 1.5-3 |
| JUMBO | +/- $1^1/_2$ | 19-35 | 12.75-20+mm | M-Q+ | 9-30+mm | 6-7 | Chunky/Roving | .75-1 |

**EFG**: Extra Fine Gauge | **FG**: Fine Gauge | **SG**: Small Gauge |**RG**: Regular Gauge | **LG**: Large Gauge | **XLG**: Extra Large Gauge | **JUMBO**: Jumbo

Knit & Crochet Planner          goodknitkisses.com

# PROJECT PAGE

## PROJECT

Name: _____    Start Date: _____

Made for: _____    End Date: _____

## PATTERN

Pattern: _____

Source: _____
(Website / Book / Magazine)

Gauge: ____ sts X ____ rows in _____ in/cm

Size: _____

## YARN

| Name | Color | # Skeins /Yds |
|------|-------|---------------|
|      |       |               |
|      |       |               |
|      |       |               |
|      |       |               |

Attach Yarn Label(s) Here

## MATERIALS

### Needle/Hook/Loom

| Name/Brand/Style | Size |
|------------------|------|
|                  |      |
|                  |      |
|                  |      |
|                  |      |

### Other Materials

| | |
|---|---|
| ○ tapestry needle | ○ |
| ○ stitch marker(s) _____ | ○ |
| ○ | ○ |

Remove this page and keep it with your project for a quick reference.

Knit & Crochet Planner                goodknitkisses.com

## PROJECT NOTES

_____

_____

_____

_____

_____

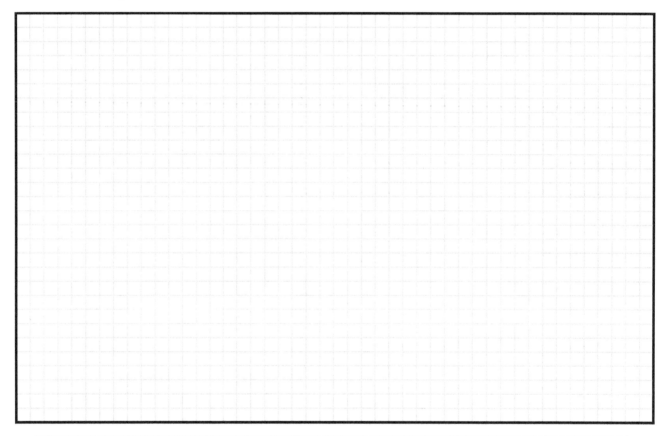

| Loom-Needle-Hook Equivalence Chart with Recommended Yarn Weight | | | | | | | | |
|---|---|---|---|---|---|---|---|---|
| Loom Size | | Needle Size | | Hook Size | | Yarn Weight | | |
| Gauge | Peg C2C (in.) | US | mm | US | mm | US | UK/AU | Avg. sts/in |
| EFG | $^3/_{16}$ | 1-3 | 2.25-3.25mm | A-D | 2-3.125mm | 0-2 | 1-3 ply | 7-8 |
| FG | $^1/_4$ | 3-6 | 3.25-4mm | D-G | 3.125-4.25mm | 1-3 | 2,4 & 8-ply | 5-7 |
| SG | $^5/_{16}$, $^3/_8$, $^7/_{16}$ | 5-8 | 3.75-5mm | F-H | 3.75-5mm | 2-4 | 2,4 & 8-ply,DK | 4-5 |
| RG | $^1/_2$, $^9/_{16}$ | 8-10 | 5-6mm | H-J | 5-5.75mm | 4-5 | 8-12-ply/DK/Aran | 3-4 |
| LG | $^5/_8$, $^{11}/_{16}$ | 10-13 | 6-9mm | J-M | 5.75-9mm | 5-6 | 10-12-ply/Aran/Chunky | 2-3 |
| XLG | $^3/_4$, $^{13}/_{16}$, $^7/_8$, $^{15}/_{16}$ | 13-15 | 9-10mm | M-N+ | 9-10mm | 6-7 | 12-ply/Chunky | 1.5-3 |
| JUMBO | +/- 1$^1/_2$ | 19-35 | 12.75-20+mm | M-Q+ | 9-30+mm | 6-7 | Chunky/Roving | .75-1 |

**EFG**: Extra Fine Gauge | **FG**: Fine Gauge | **SG**: Small Gauge |**RG**: Regular Gauge | **LG**: Large Gauge | **XLG**: Extra Large Gauge | **JUMBO**: Jumbo

Knit & Crochet Planner  goodknitkisses.com

# PROJECT PAGE

## PROJECT

Name: _____     Start Date: _____

Made for: _____     End Date: _____

## PATTERN

Pattern: _____

Source: _____
(Website / Book / Magazine)

Gauge: _____ sts X _____ rows in _____ in/cm

Size: _____

## YARN

| Name | Color | # Skeins /Yds |
|------|-------|---------------|
|      |       |               |
|      |       |               |
|      |       |               |
|      |       |               |

Attach Yarn Label(s) Here

## MATERIALS

### Needle/Hook/Loom

| Name/Brand/Style | Size |
|------------------|------|
|                  |      |
|                  |      |
|                  |      |
|                  |      |

### Other Materials

| ◯ tapestry needle | ◯ |
|-------------------|---|
| ◯ stitch marker(s) _____ | ◯ |
| ◯ | ◯ |

Remove this page and keep it with your project for a quick reference.

Knit & Crochet Planner          goodknitkisses.com

# PROJECT NOTES

_____

_____

_____

_____

_____

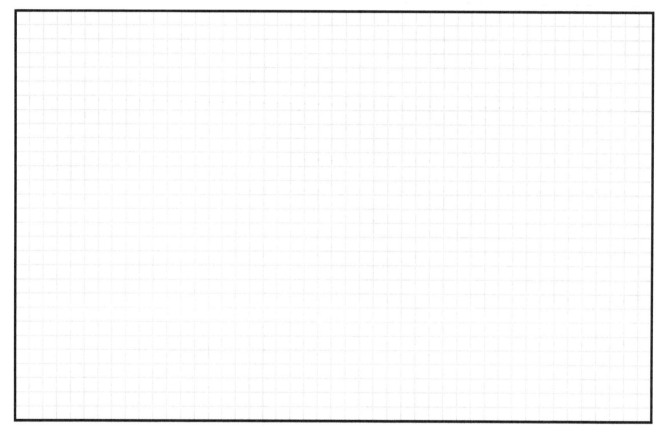

| Loom-Needle-Hook Equivalence Chart with Recommended Yarn Weight | | | | | | | | | |
|---|---|---|---|---|---|---|---|---|---|
| Loom Size | | Needle Size | | Hook Size | | Yarn Weight | | | |
| Gauge | Peg C2C (in.) | US | mm | US | mm | US | UK/AU | Avg. sts/in |
| EFG | 3/16 | 1-3 | 2.25-3.25mm | A-D | 2-3.125mm | 0-2 | 1-3 ply | 7-8 |
| FG | 1/4 | 3-6 | 3.25-4mm | D-G | 3.125-4.25mm | 1-3 | 2,4 & 8-ply | 5-7 |
| SG | 5/16, 3/8, 7/16 | 5-8 | 3.75-5mm | F-H | 3.75-5mm | 2-4 | 2,4 & 8-ply,DK | 4-5 |
| RG | 1/2, 9/16 | 8-10 | 5-6mm | H-J | 5-5.75mm | 4-5 | 8-12-ply/DK/Aran | 3-4 |
| LG | 5/8, 11/16 | 10-13 | 6-9mm | J-M | 5.75-9mm | 5-6 | 10-12-ply/Aran/Chunky | 2-3 |
| XLG | 3/4, 13/16, 7/8, 15/16 | 13-15 | 9-10mm | M-N+ | 9-10mm | 6-7 | 12-ply/Chunky | 1.5-3 |
| JUMBO | +/- 1 1/2 | 19-35 | 12.75-20+mm | M-Q+ | 9-30+mm | 6-7 | Chunky/Roving | .75-1 |

**EFG**: Extra Fine Gauge | **FG**: Fine Gauge | **SG**: Small Gauge | **RG**: Regular Gauge | **LG**: Large Gauge | **XLG**: Extra Large Gauge | **JUMBO**: Jumbo

Knit & Crochet Planner        goodknitkisses.com

# PROJECT PAGE

PROJECT

## PROJECT

Name: ______________________ Start Date: ______________

Made for: ______________________ End Date: ______________

## PATTERN

Pattern: ______________________

Source: ______________________
(Website / Book / Magazine)

Gauge: ____ sts X ____ rows in ______ in/cm

Size: ______________________

## YARN

| Name | Color | # Skeins /Yds |
|---|---|---|
| | | |
| | | |
| | | |
| | | |

Attach Yarn Label(s) Here

## MATERIALS

Needle/Hook/Loom

| Name/Brand/Style | Size |
|---|---|
| | |
| | |
| | |
| | |

Other Materials

| | |
|---|---|
| ◯ tapestry needle | ◯ |
| ◯ stitch marker(s) _____ | ◯ |
| ◯ | ◯ |

Remove this page and keep it with your project for a quick reference.

PROJECT

# PROJECT NOTES

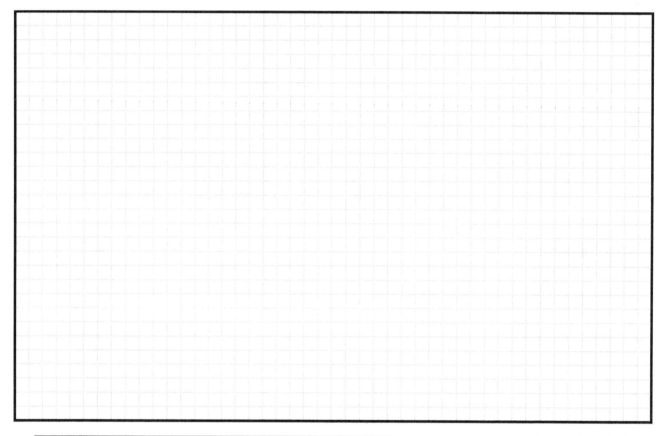

| Loom-Needle-Hook Equivalence Chart with Recommended Yarn Weight | | | | | | | | |
|---|---|---|---|---|---|---|---|---|
| Loom Size | | Needle Size | | Hook Size | | Yarn Weight | | |
| Gauge | Peg C2C (in.) | US | mm | US | mm | US | UK/AU | Avg. sts/in |
| EFG | ³/₁₆ | 1-3 | 2.25-3.25mm | A-D | 2-3.125mm | 0-2 | 1-3 ply | 7-8 |
| FG | ¼ | 3-6 | 3.25-4mm | D-G | 3.125-4.25mm | 1-3 | 2,4 & 8-ply | 5-7 |
| SG | ⁵/₁₆, ³/₈, ⁷/₁₆ | 5-8 | 3.75-5mm | F-H | 3.75-5mm | 2-4 | 2,4 & 8-ply,DK | 4-5 |
| RG | ½, ⁹/₁₆ | 8-10 | 5-6mm | H-J | 5-5.75mm | 4-5 | 8-12-ply/DK/Aran | 3-4 |
| LG | ⁵/₈, ¹¹/₁₆ | 10-13 | 6-9mm | J-M | 5.75-9mm | 5-6 | 10-12-ply/Aran/Chunky | 2-3 |
| XLG | ³/₄, ¹³/₁₆, ⁷/₈, ¹⁵/₁₆ | 13-15 | 9-10mm | M-N+ | 9-10mm | 6-7 | 12-ply/Chunky | 1.5-3 |
| JUMBO | +/- 1½ | 19-35 | 12.75-20+mm | M-Q+ | 9-30+mm | 6-7 | Chunky/Roving | .75-1 |

**EFG**: Extra Fine Gauge | **FG**: Fine Gauge | **SG**: Small Gauge |**RG**: Regular Gauge | **LG**: Large Gauge | **XLG**: Extra Large Gauge | **JUMBO**: Jumbo

Knit & Crochet Planner                    goodknitkisses.com

# PROJECT PAGE

## PROJECT

Name: _____    Start Date: _____

Made for: _____    End Date: _____

## PATTERN

Pattern: _____

Source: _____
(Website / Book / Magazine)

Gauge: _____ sts X _____ rows in _____ in/cm

Size: _____

## YARN

| Name | Color | # Skeins /Yds |
|------|-------|---------------|
|      |       |               |
|      |       |               |
|      |       |               |
|      |       |               |

Attach Yarn Label(s) Here

## MATERIALS

### Needle/Hook/Loom

| Name/Brand/Style | Size |
|------------------|------|
|                  |      |
|                  |      |
|                  |      |
|                  |      |

### Other Materials

| | |
|---|---|
| ○ tapestry needle | ○ |
| ○ stitch marker(s) _____ | ○ |
| ○ | ○ |

Remove this page and keep it with your project for a quick reference.

Knit & Crochet Planner        goodknitkisses.com

## PROJECT NOTES

_____

_____

_____

_____

_____

_____

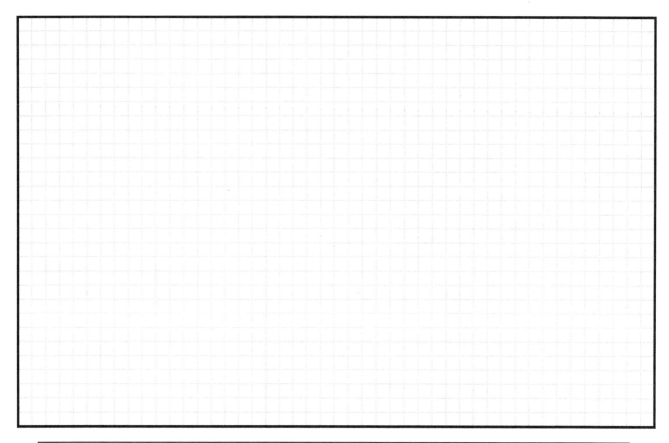

| Loom-Needle-Hook Equivalence Chart with Recommended Yarn Weight | | | | | | | | |
|---|---|---|---|---|---|---|---|---|
| Loom Size | | Needle Size | | Hook Size | | Yarn Weight | | |
| Gauge | Peg C2C (in.) | US | mm | US | mm | US | UK/AU | Avg. sts/in |
| EFG | 3/16 | 1-3 | 2.25-3.25mm | A-D | 2-3.125mm | 0-2 | 1-3 ply | 7-8 |
| FG | 1/4 | 3-6 | 3.25-4mm | D-G | 3.125-4.25mm | 1-3 | 2,4 & 8-ply | 5-7 |
| SG | 5/16, 3/8, 7/16 | 5-8 | 3.75-5mm | F-H | 3.75-5mm | 2-4 | 2,4 & 8-ply,DK | 4-5 |
| RG | 1/2, 9/16 | 8-10 | 5-6mm | H-J | 5-5.75mm | 4-5 | 8-12-ply/DK/Aran | 3-4 |
| LG | 5/8, 11/16 | 10-13 | 6-9mm | J-M | 5.75-9mm | 5-6 | 10-12-ply/Aran/Chunky | 2-3 |
| XLG | 3/4, 13/16, 7/8, 15/16 | 13-15 | 9-10mm | M-N+ | 9-10mm | 6-7 | 12-ply/Chunky | 1.5-3 |
| JUMBO | +/- 1 1/2 | 19-35 | 12.75-20+mm | M-Q+ | 9-30+mm | 6-7 | Chunky/Roving | .75-1 |

**EFG**: Extra Fine Gauge | **FG**: Fine Gauge | **SG**: Small Gauge | **RG**: Regular Gauge | **LG**: Large Gauge | **XLG**: Extra Large Gauge | **JUMBO**: Jumbo

# PROJECT PAGE

## PROJECT

Name: _____     Start Date: _____

Made for: _____     End Date: _____

## PATTERN

Pattern: _____

Source: _____
             (Website / Book / Magazine)

Gauge: _____ sts X _____ rows in _____ in/cm

Size: _____

## YARN

| Name | Color | # Skeins /Yds |
|------|-------|---------------|
|      |       |               |
|      |       |               |
|      |       |               |
|      |       |               |

Attach Yarn Label(s) Here

## MATERIALS

### Needle/Hook/Loom

| Name/Brand/Style | Size |
|------------------|------|
|                  |      |
|                  |      |
|                  |      |
|                  |      |

### Other Materials

| ○ tapestry needle | ○ |
|-------------------|---|
| ○ stitch marker(s) _____ | ○ |
| ○ | ○ |

Remove this page and keep it with your project for a quick reference.

Knit & Crochet Planner          goodknitkisses.com

PROJECT

# PROJECT NOTES

_____

_____

_____

_____

_____

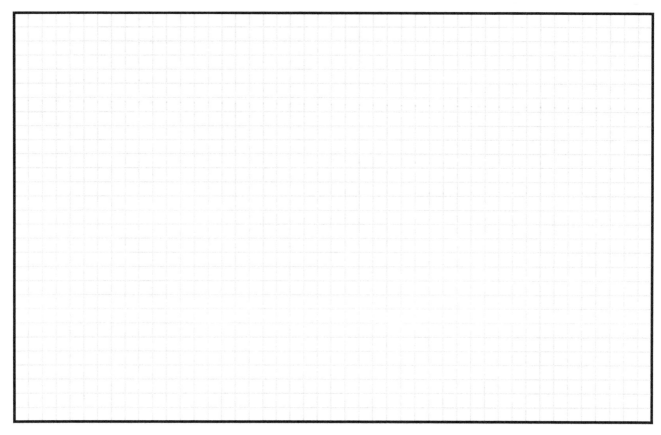

| Loom-Needle-Hook Equivalence Chart with Recommended Yarn Weight | | | | | | | | |
|---|---|---|---|---|---|---|---|---|
| Loom Size | | Needle Size | | Hook Size | | Yarn Weight | | |
| Gauge | Peg C2C (in.) | US | mm | US | mm | US | UK/AU | Avg. sts/in |
| EFG | $^3/_{16}$ | 1-3 | 2.25-3.25mm | A-D | 2-3.125mm | 0-2 | 1-3 ply | 7-8 |
| FG | $^1/_4$ | 3-6 | 3.25-4mm | D-G | 3.125-4.25mm | 1-3 | 2,4 & 8-ply | 5-7 |
| SG | $^5/_{16}, ^3/_8, ^7/_{16}$ | 5-8 | 3.75-5mm | F-H | 3.75-5mm | 2-4 | 2,4 & 8-ply,DK | 4-5 |
| RG | $^1/_2, ^9/_{16}$ | 8-10 | 5-6mm | H-J | 5-5.75mm | 4-5 | 8-12-ply/DK/Aran | 3-4 |
| LG | $^5/_8, ^{11}/_{16}$ | 10-13 | 6-9mm | J-M | 5.75-9mm | 5-6 | 10-12-ply/Aran/Chunky | 2-3 |
| XLG | $^3/_4, ^{13}/_{16}, ^7/_8, ^{15}/_{16}$ | 13-15 | 9-10mm | M-N+ | 9-10mm | 6-7 | 12-ply/Chunky | 1.5-3 |
| JUMBO | +/- $1^1/_2$ | 19-35 | 12.75-20+mm | M-Q+ | 9-30+mm | 6-7 | Chunky/Roving | .75-1 |

**EFG**: Extra Fine Gauge | **FG**: Fine Gauge | **SG**: Small Gauge | **RG**: Regular Gauge | **LG**: Large Gauge | **XLG**: Extra Large Gauge | **JUMBO**: Jumbo

Knit & Crochet Planner  goodknitkisses.com

# ADDITIONAL PROJECT NOTES

Knit & Crochet Planner          goodknitkisses.com

PROJECT

# ADDITIONAL PROJECT NOTES

PROJECT

# PROJECT GRAPH

Knit & Crochet Planner          goodknitkisses.com

# ADDITIONAL PROJECT NOTES

PROJECT

# ADDITIONAL PROJECT NOTES

**PROJECT**

# PROJECT GRAPH

# ADDITIONAL PROJECT NOTES

# PROJECT GRAPH

# ADDITIONAL PROJECT NOTES

PROJECT

# ADDITIONAL PROJECT NOTES

PROJECT

PROJECT

# ADDITIONAL PROJECT NOTES

# PROJECT GRAPH

PROJECT

# ADDITIONAL PROJECT NOTES

Knit & Crochet Planner                goodknitkisses.com

PROJECT

# ADDITIONAL PROJECT NOTES

PROJECT

Knit & Crochet Planner

goodknitkisses.com

PROJECT

# CHARITABLE DONATION CHECKLIST

## ORGANIZATION

Name: _____

Phone: _____

Contact: _____

Email: _____

Position: _____

Drop Off Location: _____

Drop Off Hours: _____

_____

_____

Do they issue a Tax Receipt?  ☐ Yes   ☐ No

Info for Receipt (cost of materials, …):

_____

## ITEM GUIDELINES

Accepted Items: _____

Size(s): _____

_____

_____

_____

_____

Restrictions: Hat Brim Style: _____

Buttons:  ☐ Yes   ☐ No

Earflaps:  ☐ Yes   ☐ No

Tassels:  ☐ Yes   ☐ No

Patches:  ☐ Yes   ☐ No

Pom Poms:  ☐ Yes   ☐ No

## ALLERGY GUIDELINES

Accepted Yarns:  ☐ All yarn accepted   ☐ Acrylic   ☐ Cotton   ☐ Alpaca

☐ Wool   ☐ Bamboo   ☐ Other:_____

Other Restrictions:  ☐ Smoke-free Home   ☐ Prewash itesms

☐ Pet-free Home   ☐ Do NOT prewash items

Knit & Crochet Planner          goodknitkisses.com

# CHARITABLE DONATION LOG

| Date | Organization | Donated Items | Value | Receipt |
|------|--------------|---------------|-------|---------|
|      |              |               |       | ☐ |
|      |              |               |       | ☐ |
|      |              |               |       | ☐ |
|      |              |               |       | ☐ |
|      |              |               |       | ☐ |
|      |              |               |       | ☐ |
|      |              |               |       | ☐ |
|      |              |               |       | ☐ |
|      |              |               |       | ☐ |
|      |              |               |       | ☐ |
|      |              |               |       | ☐ |
|      |              |               |       | ☐ |
|      |              |               |       | ☐ |
|      |              |               |       | ☐ |
|      |              |               |       | ☐ |
|      |              |               |       | ☐ |
|      |              |               |       | ☐ |
|      |              |               |       | ☐ |
|      |              |               |       | ☐ |
|      |              |               |       | ☐ |
|      |              |               |       | ☐ |

LOGS

# CHARITABLE DONATION CHECKLIST

## ORGANIZATION

Name: _____

Phone: _____

Contact: _____

Email: _____

Position: _____

Drop Off Location: _____

Drop Off Hours: _____

_____

_____

Do they issue a Tax Receipt?  ☐ Yes   ☐ No

Info for Receipt (cost of materials, …):

_____

## ITEM GUIDELINES

Accepted Items: _____

_____

_____

Size(s): _____

_____

_____

Restrictions: Hat Brim Style: _____

Buttons:  ☐ Yes   ☐ No

Earflaps:  ☐ Yes   ☐ No

Tassels:  ☐ Yes   ☐ No

Patches:  ☐ Yes   ☐ No

Pom Poms:  ☐ Yes   ☐ No

## ALLERGY GUIDELINES

Accepted Yarns:  ☐ All yarn accepted   ☐ Acrylic   ☐ Cotton   ☐ Alpaca

☐ Wool   ☐ Bamboo   ☐ Other:_____

Other Restrictions:  ☐ Smoke-free Home   ☐ Prewash itesms

☐ Pet-free Home   ☐ Do NOT prewash items

Knit & Crochet Planner      goodknitkisses.com

# CHARITABLE DONATION LOG

| Date | Organization | Donated Items | Value | Receipt |
|------|--------------|---------------|-------|---------|
|      |              |               |       | ☐ |
|      |              |               |       | ☐ |
|      |              |               |       | ☐ |
|      |              |               |       | ☐ |
|      |              |               |       | ☐ |
|      |              |               |       | ☐ |
|      |              |               |       | ☐ |
|      |              |               |       | ☐ |
|      |              |               |       | ☐ |
|      |              |               |       | ☐ |
|      |              |               |       | ☐ |
|      |              |               |       | ☐ |
|      |              |               |       | ☐ |
|      |              |               |       | ☐ |
|      |              |               |       | ☐ |
|      |              |               |       | ☐ |
|      |              |               |       | ☐ |
|      |              |               |       | ☐ |
|      |              |               |       | ☐ |
|      |              |               |       | ☐ |
|      |              |               |       | ☐ |
|      |              |               |       | ☐ |

LOGS

# CHARITABLE DONATION CHECKLIST

## ORGANIZATION

Name: _____

Phone: _____

Contact: _____

Email: _____

Position: _____

Drop Off Location: _____

Drop Off Hours: _____

_____

_____

Do they issue a Tax Receipt? ☐ Yes ☐ No

Info for Receipt (cost of materials, …):

_____

## ITEM GUIDELINES

Accepted Items: _____

Size(s): _____

_____

_____

_____

_____

Restrictions: Hat Brim Style: _____

Buttons: ☐ Yes ☐ No

Earflaps: ☐ Yes ☐ No

Tassels: ☐ Yes ☐ No

Patches: ☐ Yes ☐ No

Pom Poms: ☐ Yes ☐ No

## ALLERGY GUIDELINES

Accepted Yarns: ☐ All yarn accepted ☐ Acrylic ☐ Cotton ☐ Alpaca

☐ Wool ☐ Bamboo ☐ Other:_____

Other Restrictions: ☐ Smoke-free Home ☐ Prewash itesms

☐ Pet-free Home ☐ Do NOT prewash items

Knit & Crochet Planner  goodknitkisses.com

# CHARITABLE DONATION LOG

| Date | Organization | Donated Items | Value | Receipt |
|------|--------------|---------------|-------|:-------:|
|  |  |  |  | ☐ |
|  |  |  |  | ☐ |
|  |  |  |  | ☐ |
|  |  |  |  | ☐ |
|  |  |  |  | ☐ |
|  |  |  |  | ☐ |
|  |  |  |  | ☐ |
|  |  |  |  | ☐ |
|  |  |  |  | ☐ |
|  |  |  |  | ☐ |
|  |  |  |  | ☐ |
|  |  |  |  | ☐ |
|  |  |  |  | ☐ |
|  |  |  |  | ☐ |
|  |  |  |  | ☐ |
|  |  |  |  | ☐ |
|  |  |  |  | ☐ |
|  |  |  |  | ☐ |
|  |  |  |  | ☐ |
|  |  |  |  | ☐ |
|  |  |  |  | ☐ |
|  |  |  |  | ☐ |

LOGS

Knit & Crochet Planner          goodknitkisses.com

# CHARITABLE DONATION CHECKLIST

## ORGANIZATION

Name: _____     Phone: _____

Contact: _____     Email: _____

Position: _____

Drop Off Location: _____     Drop Off Hours: _____

_____

_____

Do they issue a Tax Receipt?     ☐ Yes     Info for Receipt (cost of materials, …):
                                  ☐ No      _____

## ITEM GUIDELINES

Accepted Items: _____     Size(s): _____

_____     _____

_____     _____

Restrictions: Hat Brim Style: _____     Buttons: ☐ Yes   ☐ No

Earflaps: ☐ Yes   ☐ No     Tassels: ☐ Yes   ☐ No

Patches: ☐ Yes   ☐ No     Pom Poms: ☐ Yes   ☐ No

## ALLERGY GUIDELINES

Accepted Yarns: ☐ All yarn accepted   ☐ Acrylic   ☐ Cotton   ☐ Alpaca

☐ Wool   ☐ Bamboo   ☐ Other: _____

Other Restrictions: ☐ Smoke-free Home   ☐ Prewash itesms

☐ Pet-free Home   ☐ Do NOT prewash items

# CHARITABLE DONATION LOG

| Date | Organization | Donated Items | Value | Receipt |
|------|-------------|---------------|-------|---------|
|      |             |               |       | ☐ |
|      |             |               |       | ☐ |
|      |             |               |       | ☐ |
|      |             |               |       | ☐ |
|      |             |               |       | ☐ |
|      |             |               |       | ☐ |
|      |             |               |       | ☐ |
|      |             |               |       | ☐ |
|      |             |               |       | ☐ |
|      |             |               |       | ☐ |
|      |             |               |       | ☐ |
|      |             |               |       | ☐ |
|      |             |               |       | ☐ |
|      |             |               |       | ☐ |
|      |             |               |       | ☐ |
|      |             |               |       | ☐ |
|      |             |               |       | ☐ |
|      |             |               |       | ☐ |
|      |             |               |       | ☐ |
|      |             |               |       | ☐ |
|      |             |               |       | ☐ |
|      |             |               |       | ☐ |

LOGS

Knit & Crochet Planner          goodknitkisses.com

# GIFT GIVING LIST

| Date | Occasion | Name | Item |
|------|----------|------|------|
|      |          |      |      |
|      |          |      |      |
|      |          |      |      |
|      |          |      |      |
|      |          |      |      |
|      |          |      |      |
|      |          |      |      |
|      |          |      |      |
|      |          |      |      |
|      |          |      |      |
|      |          |      |      |
|      |          |      |      |
|      |          |      |      |
|      |          |      |      |
|      |          |      |      |
|      |          |      |      |
|      |          |      |      |
|      |          |      |      |
|      |          |      |      |
|      |          |      |      |
|      |          |      |      |
|      |          |      |      |
|      |          |      |      |

Knit & Crochet Planner  goodknitkisses.com

# GIFT GIVING LIST

| Date | Occasion | Name | Item |
|------|----------|------|------|
|      |          |      |      |
|      |          |      |      |
|      |          |      |      |
|      |          |      |      |
|      |          |      |      |
|      |          |      |      |
|      |          |      |      |
|      |          |      |      |
|      |          |      |      |
|      |          |      |      |
|      |          |      |      |
|      |          |      |      |
|      |          |      |      |
|      |          |      |      |
|      |          |      |      |
|      |          |      |      |
|      |          |      |      |
|      |          |      |      |
|      |          |      |      |
|      |          |      |      |
|      |          |      |      |

# GIFT GIVING LIST

| Date | Occasion | Name | Item |
|------|----------|------|------|
|      |          |      |      |
|      |          |      |      |
|      |          |      |      |
|      |          |      |      |
|      |          |      |      |
|      |          |      |      |
|      |          |      |      |
|      |          |      |      |
|      |          |      |      |
|      |          |      |      |
|      |          |      |      |
|      |          |      |      |
|      |          |      |      |
|      |          |      |      |
|      |          |      |      |
|      |          |      |      |
|      |          |      |      |
|      |          |      |      |
|      |          |      |      |
|      |          |      |      |
|      |          |      |      |
|      |          |      |      |
|      |          |      |      |

LOGS

Knit & Crochet Planner  goodknitkisses.com

# GIFT GIVING LIST

| Date | Occasion | Name | Item |
|------|----------|------|------|
|      |          |      |      |
|      |          |      |      |
|      |          |      |      |
|      |          |      |      |
|      |          |      |      |
|      |          |      |      |
|      |          |      |      |
|      |          |      |      |
|      |          |      |      |
|      |          |      |      |
|      |          |      |      |
|      |          |      |      |
|      |          |      |      |
|      |          |      |      |
|      |          |      |      |
|      |          |      |      |
|      |          |      |      |
|      |          |      |      |
|      |          |      |      |
|      |          |      |      |
|      |          |      |      |

LOGS

# SALES LOG

| Date | Source | | Item | Price |
|------|--------|---|------|-------|
| | ☐ Craft Fair   ☐ Etsy/Online Sale<br>☐ Commissioned Item   ☐ _____ | | | |
| | ☐ Craft Fair   ☐ Etsy/Online Sale<br>☐ Commissioned Item   ☐ _____ | | | |
| | ☐ Craft Fair   ☐ Etsy/Online Sale<br>☐ Commissioned Item   ☐ _____ | | | |
| | ☐ Craft Fair   ☐ Etsy/Online Sale<br>☐ Commissioned Item   ☐ _____ | | | |
| | ☐ Craft Fair   ☐ Etsy/Online Sale<br>☐ Commissioned Item   ☐ _____ | | | |
| | ☐ Craft Fair   ☐ Etsy/Online Sale<br>☐ Commissioned Item   ☐ _____ | | | |
| | ☐ Craft Fair   ☐ Etsy/Online Sale<br>☐ Commissioned Item   ☐ _____ | | | |
| | ☐ Craft Fair   ☐ Etsy/Online Sale<br>☐ Commissioned Item   ☐ _____ | | | |
| | ☐ Craft Fair   ☐ Etsy/Online Sale<br>☐ Commissioned Item   ☐ _____ | | | |
| | ☐ Craft Fair   ☐ Etsy/Online Sale<br>☐ Commissioned Item   ☐ _____ | | | |
| | ☐ Craft Fair   ☐ Etsy/Online Sale<br>☐ Commissioned Item   ☐ _____ | | | |
| | ☐ Craft Fair   ☐ Etsy/Online Sale<br>☐ Commissioned Item   ☐ _____ | | | |
| | ☐ Craft Fair   ☐ Etsy/Online Sale<br>☐ Commissioned Item   ☐ _____ | | | |
| | ☐ Craft Fair   ☐ Etsy/Online Sale<br>☐ Commissioned Item   ☐ _____ | | | |

LOGS

Knit & Crochet Planner        goodknitkisses.com

# SALES LOG

| Date | Source | | Item | Price |
|------|--------|--|------|-------|
| | ☐ Craft Fair    ☐ Etsy/Online Sale <br> ☐ Commissioned Item    ☐ _____ | | | |
| | ☐ Craft Fair    ☐ Etsy/Online Sale <br> ☐ Commissioned Item    ☐ _____ | | | |
| | ☐ Craft Fair    ☐ Etsy/Online Sale <br> ☐ Commissioned Item    ☐ _____ | | | |
| | ☐ Craft Fair    ☐ Etsy/Online Sale <br> ☐ Commissioned Item    ☐ _____ | | | |
| | ☐ Craft Fair    ☐ Etsy/Online Sale <br> ☐ Commissioned Item    ☐ _____ | | | |
| | ☐ Craft Fair    ☐ Etsy/Online Sale <br> ☐ Commissioned Item    ☐ _____ | | | |
| | ☐ Craft Fair    ☐ Etsy/Online Sale <br> ☐ Commissioned Item    ☐ _____ | | | |
| | ☐ Craft Fair    ☐ Etsy/Online Sale <br> ☐ Commissioned Item    ☐ _____ | | | |
| | ☐ Craft Fair    ☐ Etsy/Online Sale <br> ☐ Commissioned Item    ☐ _____ | | | |
| | ☐ Craft Fair    ☐ Etsy/Online Sale <br> ☐ Commissioned Item    ☐ _____ | | | |
| | ☐ Craft Fair    ☐ Etsy/Online Sale <br> ☐ Commissioned Item    ☐ _____ | | | |
| | ☐ Craft Fair    ☐ Etsy/Online Sale <br> ☐ Commissioned Item    ☐ _____ | | | |
| | ☐ Craft Fair    ☐ Etsy/Online Sale <br> ☐ Commissioned Item    ☐ _____ | | | |
| | ☐ Craft Fair    ☐ Etsy/Online Sale <br> ☐ Commissioned Item    ☐ _____ | | | |

**LOGS**

Knit & Crochet Planner      goodknitkisses.com

# SALES LOG

| Date | Source | | Item | Price |
|------|--------|--|------|-------|
| | ☐ Craft Fair     ☐ Etsy/Online Sale<br>☐ Commissioned Item     ☐ _____ | | | |
| | ☐ Craft Fair     ☐ Etsy/Online Sale<br>☐ Commissioned Item     ☐ _____ | | | |
| | ☐ Craft Fair     ☐ Etsy/Online Sale<br>☐ Commissioned Item     ☐ _____ | | | |
| | ☐ Craft Fair     ☐ Etsy/Online Sale<br>☐ Commissioned Item     ☐ _____ | | | |
| | ☐ Craft Fair     ☐ Etsy/Online Sale<br>☐ Commissioned Item     ☐ _____ | | | |
| | ☐ Craft Fair     ☐ Etsy/Online Sale<br>☐ Commissioned Item     ☐ _____ | | | |
| | ☐ Craft Fair     ☐ Etsy/Online Sale<br>☐ Commissioned Item     ☐ _____ | | | |
| | ☐ Craft Fair     ☐ Etsy/Online Sale<br>☐ Commissioned Item     ☐ _____ | | | |
| | ☐ Craft Fair     ☐ Etsy/Online Sale<br>☐ Commissioned Item     ☐ _____ | | | |
| | ☐ Craft Fair     ☐ Etsy/Online Sale<br>☐ Commissioned Item     ☐ _____ | | | |
| | ☐ Craft Fair     ☐ Etsy/Online Sale<br>☐ Commissioned Item     ☐ _____ | | | |
| | ☐ Craft Fair     ☐ Etsy/Online Sale<br>☐ Commissioned Item     ☐ _____ | | | |
| | ☐ Craft Fair     ☐ Etsy/Online Sale<br>☐ Commissioned Item     ☐ _____ | | | |

# SALES LOG

| Date | Source | | Item | Price |
|------|--------|---|------|-------|
| | ☐ Craft Fair      ☐ Etsy/Online Sale<br>☐ Commissioned Item      ☐ _____ | | | |
| | ☐ Craft Fair      ☐ Etsy/Online Sale<br>☐ Commissioned Item      ☐ _____ | | | |
| | ☐ Craft Fair      ☐ Etsy/Online Sale<br>☐ Commissioned Item      ☐ _____ | | | |
| | ☐ Craft Fair      ☐ Etsy/Online Sale<br>☐ Commissioned Item      ☐ _____ | | | |
| | ☐ Craft Fair      ☐ Etsy/Online Sale<br>☐ Commissioned Item      ☐ _____ | | | |
| | ☐ Craft Fair      ☐ Etsy/Online Sale<br>☐ Commissioned Item      ☐ _____ | | | |
| | ☐ Craft Fair      ☐ Etsy/Online Sale<br>☐ Commissioned Item      ☐ _____ | | | |
| | ☐ Craft Fair      ☐ Etsy/Online Sale<br>☐ Commissioned Item      ☐ _____ | | | |
| | ☐ Craft Fair      ☐ Etsy/Online Sale<br>☐ Commissioned Item      ☐ _____ | | | |
| | ☐ Craft Fair      ☐ Etsy/Online Sale<br>☐ Commissioned Item      ☐ _____ | | | |
| | ☐ Craft Fair      ☐ Etsy/Online Sale<br>☐ Commissioned Item      ☐ _____ | | | |
| | ☐ Craft Fair      ☐ Etsy/Online Sale<br>☐ Commissioned Item      ☐ _____ | | | |
| | ☐ Craft Fair      ☐ Etsy/Online Sale<br>☐ Commissioned Item      ☐ _____ | | | |
| | ☐ Craft Fair      ☐ Etsy/Online Sale<br>☐ Commissioned Item      ☐ _____ | | | |

# LOOM INVENTORY

| Brand | Gauge | Peg Spacing | # of Pegs | Type | | Other (Material, Color, ...) |
|---|---|---|---|---|---|---|
| | | | | ☐ Round | ☐ Long | |
| | | | | ☐ S-loom | ☐ _____ | |
| | | | | ☐ Round | ☐ Long | |
| | | | | ☐ S-loom | ☐ _____ | |
| | | | | ☐ Round | ☐ Long | |
| | | | | ☐ S-loom | ☐ _____ | |
| | | | | ☐ Round | ☐ Long | |
| | | | | ☐ S-loom | ☐ _____ | |
| | | | | ☐ Round | ☐ Long | |
| | | | | ☐ S-loom | ☐ _____ | |
| | | | | ☐ Round | ☐ Long | |
| | | | | ☐ S-loom | ☐ _____ | |
| | | | | ☐ Round | ☐ Long | |
| | | | | ☐ S-loom | ☐ _____ | |
| | | | | ☐ Round | ☐ Long | |
| | | | | ☐ S-loom | ☐ _____ | |
| | | | | ☐ Round | ☐ Long | |
| | | | | ☐ S-loom | ☐ _____ | |
| | | | | ☐ Round | ☐ Long | |
| | | | | ☐ S-loom | ☐ _____ | |
| | | | | ☐ Round | ☐ Long | |
| | | | | ☐ S-loom | ☐ _____ | |
| | | | | ☐ Round | ☐ Long | |
| | | | | ☐ S-loom | ☐ _____ | |
| | | | | ☐ Round | ☐ Long | |
| | | | | ☐ S-loom | ☐ _____ | |
| | | | | ☐ Round | ☐ Long | |
| | | | | ☐ S-loom | ☐ _____ | |

## Loom Gauge Reference with Center to Center Peg Measurement (in.)

| | | | | | |
|---|---|---|---|---|---|
| EFG - Extra Fine Gauge | $\frac{3}{16}$ | SG - Small Gauge | $\frac{5}{16}, \frac{3}{8}, \frac{7}{16}$ | LG - Large Gauge | $\frac{5}{8}, \frac{11}{16}$ |
| FG - Fine Gauge | $\frac{1}{4}$ | RG - Regular Gauge | $\frac{1}{2}, \frac{9}{16}$ | XLG - Extra Large Gauge | $\frac{3}{4}, \frac{13}{16}, \frac{7}{8}, \frac{15}{16}$ |
| | | | | JUMBO - Jumbo Gauge | +/- $1\frac{1}{2}$ |

INVENTORY

Knit & Crochet Planner  goodknitkisses.com

# LOOM INVENTORY

| Brand | Gauge | Peg Spacing | # of Pegs | Type | | Other (Material, Color, ...) |
|---|---|---|---|---|---|---|
| | | | | ☐ Round | ☐ Long | |
| | | | | ☐ S-loom | ☐ _____ | |
| | | | | ☐ Round | ☐ Long | |
| | | | | ☐ S-loom | ☐ _____ | |
| | | | | ☐ Round | ☐ Long | |
| | | | | ☐ S-loom | ☐ _____ | |
| | | | | ☐ Round | ☐ Long | |
| | | | | ☐ S-loom | ☐ _____ | |
| | | | | ☐ Round | ☐ Long | |
| | | | | ☐ S-loom | ☐ _____ | |
| | | | | ☐ Round | ☐ Long | |
| | | | | ☐ S-loom | ☐ _____ | |
| | | | | ☐ Round | ☐ Long | |
| | | | | ☐ S-loom | ☐ _____ | |
| | | | | ☐ Round | ☐ Long | |
| | | | | ☐ S-loom | ☐ _____ | |
| | | | | ☐ Round | ☐ Long | |
| | | | | ☐ S-loom | ☐ _____ | |
| | | | | ☐ Round | ☐ Long | |
| | | | | ☐ S-loom | ☐ _____ | |
| | | | | ☐ Round | ☐ Long | |
| | | | | ☐ S-loom | ☐ _____ | |
| | | | | ☐ Round | ☐ Long | |
| | | | | ☐ S-loom | ☐ _____ | |
| | | | | ☐ Round | ☐ Long | |
| | | | | ☐ S-loom | ☐ _____ | |
| | | | | ☐ Round | ☐ Long | |
| | | | | ☐ S-loom | ☐ _____ | |
| | | | | ☐ Round | ☐ Long | |
| | | | | ☐ S-loom | ☐ _____ | |

### Loom Gauge Reference with Center to Center Peg Measurement (in.)

| EFG - Extra Fine Gauge | $^3/_{16}$ | SG - Small Gauge | $^5/_{16}$, $^3/_8$, $^7/_{16}$ | LG - Large Gauge | $^5/_8$, $^{11}/_{16}$ |
|---|---|---|---|---|---|
| FG - Fine Gauge | $^1/_4$ | RG - Regular Gauge | $^1/_2$, $^9/_{16}$ | XLG - Extra Large Gauge | $^3/_4$, $^{13}/_{16}$, $^7/_8$, $^{15}/_{16}$ |
| | | | | JUMBO - Jumbo Gauge | +/- $1^1/_2$ |

INVENTORY

Knit & Crochet Planner  goodknitkisses.com

# LOOM INVENTORY

| Brand | Gauge | Peg Spacing | # of Pegs | Type | Other (Material, Color, ...) |
|---|---|---|---|---|---|
| | | | | ☐ Round ☐ Long<br>☐ S-loom ☐ _____ | |
| | | | | ☐ Round ☐ Long<br>☐ S-loom ☐ _____ | |
| | | | | ☐ Round ☐ Long<br>☐ S-loom ☐ _____ | |
| | | | | ☐ Round ☐ Long<br>☐ S-loom ☐ _____ | |
| | | | | ☐ Round ☐ Long<br>☐ S-loom ☐ _____ | |
| | | | | ☐ Round ☐ Long<br>☐ S-loom ☐ _____ | |
| | | | | ☐ Round ☐ Long<br>☐ S-loom ☐ _____ | |
| | | | | ☐ Round ☐ Long<br>☐ S-loom ☐ _____ | |
| | | | | ☐ Round ☐ Long<br>☐ S-loom ☐ _____ | |
| | | | | ☐ Round ☐ Long<br>☐ S-loom ☐ _____ | |
| | | | | ☐ Round ☐ Long<br>☐ S-loom ☐ _____ | |
| | | | | ☐ Round ☐ Long<br>☐ S-loom ☐ _____ | |
| | | | | ☐ Round ☐ Long<br>☐ S-loom ☐ _____ | |
| | | | | ☐ Round ☐ Long<br>☐ S-loom ☐ _____ | |

## Loom Gauge Reference with Center to Center Peg Measurement (in.)

| | | | | | |
|---|---|---|---|---|---|
| EFG - Extra Fine Gauge | $\frac{3}{16}$ | SG - Small Gauge | $\frac{5}{16}$, $\frac{3}{8}$, $\frac{7}{16}$ | LG - Large Gauge | $\frac{5}{8}$, $\frac{11}{16}$ |
| FG - Fine Gauge | $\frac{1}{4}$ | RG - Regular Gauge | $\frac{1}{2}$, $\frac{9}{16}$ | XLG - Extra Large Gauge | $\frac{3}{4}$, $\frac{13}{16}$, $\frac{7}{8}$, $\frac{15}{16}$ |
| | | | | JUMBO - Jumbo Gauge | +/- $1\frac{1}{2}$ |

INVENTORY

Knit & Crochet Planner  goodknitkisses.com

# LOOM INVENTORY

| Brand | Gauge | Peg Spacing | # of Pegs | Type | | Other (Material, Color, ...) |
|-------|-------|-------------|-----------|------|--|------------------------------|
| | | | | ☐ Round  ☐ S-loom | ☐ Long  ☐ _____ | |
| | | | | ☐ Round  ☐ S-loom | ☐ Long  ☐ _____ | |
| | | | | ☐ Round  ☐ S-loom | ☐ Long  ☐ _____ | |
| | | | | ☐ Round  ☐ S-loom | ☐ Long  ☐ _____ | |
| | | | | ☐ Round  ☐ S-loom | ☐ Long  ☐ _____ | |
| | | | | ☐ Round  ☐ S-loom | ☐ Long  ☐ _____ | |
| | | | | ☐ Round  ☐ S-loom | ☐ Long  ☐ _____ | |
| | | | | ☐ Round  ☐ S-loom | ☐ Long  ☐ _____ | |
| | | | | ☐ Round  ☐ S-loom | ☐ Long  ☐ _____ | |
| | | | | ☐ Round  ☐ S-loom | ☐ Long  ☐ _____ | |
| | | | | ☐ Round  ☐ S-loom | ☐ Long  ☐ _____ | |
| | | | | ☐ Round  ☐ S-loom | ☐ Long  ☐ _____ | |
| | | | | ☐ Round  ☐ S-loom | ☐ Long  ☐ _____ | |
| | | | | ☐ Round  ☐ S-loom | ☐ Long  ☐ _____ | |

## Loom Gauge Reference with Center to Center Peg Measurement (in.)

| EFG - Extra Fine Gauge | $\frac{3}{16}$ | SG - Small Gauge | $\frac{5}{16}$, $\frac{3}{8}$, $\frac{7}{16}$ | LG - Large Gauge | $\frac{5}{8}$, $\frac{11}{16}$ |
|---|---|---|---|---|---|
| FG - Fine Gauge | $\frac{1}{4}$ | RG - Regular Gauge | $\frac{1}{2}$, $\frac{9}{16}$ | XLG - Extra Large Gauge | $\frac{3}{4}$, $\frac{13}{16}$, $\frac{7}{8}$, $\frac{15}{16}$ |
| | | | | JUMBO - Jumbo Gauge | +/- $1\frac{1}{2}$ |

**INVENTORY**

Knit & Crochet Planner                    goodknitkisses.com

# LOOM INVENTORY

| Brand | Gauge | Peg Spacing | # of Pegs | Type | | Other (Material, Color, ...) |
|-------|-------|-------------|-----------|------|---|------------------------------|
| | | | | ☐ Round ☐ S-loom | ☐ Long ☐ _____ | |
| | | | | ☐ Round ☐ S-loom | ☐ Long ☐ _____ | |
| | | | | ☐ Round ☐ S-loom | ☐ Long ☐ _____ | |
| | | | | ☐ Round ☐ S-loom | ☐ Long ☐ _____ | |
| | | | | ☐ Round ☐ S-loom | ☐ Long ☐ _____ | |
| | | | | ☐ Round ☐ S-loom | ☐ Long ☐ _____ | |
| | | | | ☐ Round ☐ S-loom | ☐ Long ☐ _____ | |
| | | | | ☐ Round ☐ S-loom | ☐ Long ☐ _____ | |
| | | | | ☐ Round ☐ S-loom | ☐ Long ☐ _____ | |
| | | | | ☐ Round ☐ S-loom | ☐ Long ☐ _____ | |
| | | | | ☐ Round ☐ S-loom | ☐ Long ☐ _____ | |
| | | | | ☐ Round ☐ S-loom | ☐ Long ☐ _____ | |
| | | | | ☐ Round ☐ S-loom | ☐ Long ☐ _____ | |
| | | | | ☐ Round ☐ S-loom | ☐ Long ☐ _____ | |

## Loom Gauge Reference with Center to Center Peg Measurement (in.)

| | | | | | |
|---|---|---|---|---|---|
| EFG - Extra Fine Gauge | 3/16 | SG - Small Gauge | 5/16, 3/8, 7/16 | LG - Large Gauge | 5/8, 11/16 |
| FG - Fine Gauge | 1/4 | RG - Regular Gauge | 1/2, 9/16 | XLG - Extra Large Gauge | 3/4, 13/16, 7/8, 15/16 |
| | | | | JUMBO - Jumbo Gauge | +/- 1 1/2 |

Knit & Crochet Planner  goodknitkisses.com

INVENTORY

# LOOM INVENTORY

| Brand | Gauge | Peg Spacing | # of Pegs | Type | | Other (Material, Color, ...) |
|---|---|---|---|---|---|---|
| | | | | ☐ Round ☐ S-loom | ☐ Long ☐ _____ | |
| | | | | ☐ Round ☐ S-loom | ☐ Long ☐ _____ | |
| | | | | ☐ Round ☐ S-loom | ☐ Long ☐ _____ | |
| | | | | ☐ Round ☐ S-loom | ☐ Long ☐ _____ | |
| | | | | ☐ Round ☐ S-loom | ☐ Long ☐ _____ | |
| | | | | ☐ Round ☐ S-loom | ☐ Long ☐ _____ | |
| | | | | ☐ Round ☐ S-loom | ☐ Long ☐ _____ | |
| | | | | ☐ Round ☐ S-loom | ☐ Long ☐ _____ | |
| | | | | ☐ Round ☐ S-loom | ☐ Long ☐ _____ | |
| | | | | ☐ Round ☐ S-loom | ☐ Long ☐ _____ | |
| | | | | ☐ Round ☐ S-loom | ☐ Long ☐ _____ | |
| | | | | ☐ Round ☐ S-loom | ☐ Long ☐ _____ | |
| | | | | ☐ Round ☐ S-loom | ☐ Long ☐ _____ | |
| | | | | ☐ Round ☐ S-loom | ☐ Long ☐ _____ | |

## Loom Gauge Reference with Center to Center Peg Measurement (in.)

| | | | | | |
|---|---|---|---|---|---|
| EFG - Extra Fine Gauge | $3/16$ | SG - Small Gauge | $5/16$, $3/8$, $7/16$ | LG - Large Gauge | $5/8$, $11/16$ |
| FG - Fine Gauge | $1/4$ | RG - Regular Gauge | $1/2$, $9/16$ | XLG - Extra Large Gauge | $3/4$, $13/16$, $7/8$, $15/16$ |
| | | | | JUMBO - Jumbo Gauge | +/- $1 1/2$ |

INVENTORY

Knit & Crochet Planner  goodknitkisses.com

# LOOM INVENTORY

| Brand | Gauge | Peg Spacing | # of Pegs | Type | | Other (Material, Color, ...) |
|-------|-------|-------------|-----------|------|---|------------------------------|
| | | | | ☐ Round  ☐ Long | ☐ S-loom  ☐ _____ | |
| | | | | ☐ Round  ☐ Long | ☐ S-loom  ☐ _____ | |
| | | | | ☐ Round  ☐ Long | ☐ S-loom  ☐ _____ | |
| | | | | ☐ Round  ☐ Long | ☐ S-loom  ☐ _____ | |
| | | | | ☐ Round  ☐ Long | ☐ S-loom  ☐ _____ | |
| | | | | ☐ Round  ☐ Long | ☐ S-loom  ☐ _____ | |
| | | | | ☐ Round  ☐ Long | ☐ S-loom  ☐ _____ | |
| | | | | ☐ Round  ☐ Long | ☐ S-loom  ☐ _____ | |
| | | | | ☐ Round  ☐ Long | ☐ S-loom  ☐ _____ | |
| | | | | ☐ Round  ☐ Long | ☐ S-loom  ☐ _____ | |
| | | | | ☐ Round  ☐ Long | ☐ S-loom  ☐ _____ | |
| | | | | ☐ Round  ☐ Long | ☐ S-loom  ☐ _____ | |
| | | | | ☐ Round  ☐ Long | ☐ S-loom  ☐ _____ | |
| | | | | ☐ Round  ☐ Long | ☐ S-loom  ☐ _____ | |

**INVENTORY**

## Loom Gauge Reference with Center to Center Peg Measurement (in.)

| EFG - Extra Fine Gauge | $\frac{3}{16}$ | SG - Small Gauge | $\frac{5}{16}, \frac{3}{8}, \frac{7}{16}$ | LG - Large Gauge | $\frac{5}{8}, \frac{11}{16}$ |
|---|---|---|---|---|---|
| FG - Fine Gauge | $\frac{1}{4}$ | RG - Regular Gauge | $\frac{1}{2}, \frac{9}{16}$ | XLG - Extra Large Gauge | $\frac{3}{4}, \frac{13}{16}, \frac{7}{8}, \frac{15}{16}$ |
| | | | | JUMBO - Jumbo Gauge | +/- $1\frac{1}{2}$ |

Knit & Crochet Planner  goodknitkisses.com

# LOOM INVENTORY

| Brand | Gauge | Peg Spacing | # of Pegs | Type | | Other (Material, Color, ...) |
|-------|-------|-------------|-----------|------|---|------------------------------|
| | | | | ☐ Round | ☐ Long | |
| | | | | ☐ S-loom | ☐ _____ | |
| | | | | ☐ Round | ☐ Long | |
| | | | | ☐ S-loom | ☐ _____ | |
| | | | | ☐ Round | ☐ Long | |
| | | | | ☐ S-loom | ☐ _____ | |
| | | | | ☐ Round | ☐ Long | |
| | | | | ☐ S-loom | ☐ _____ | |
| | | | | ☐ Round | ☐ Long | |
| | | | | ☐ S-loom | ☐ _____ | |
| | | | | ☐ Round | ☐ Long | |
| | | | | ☐ S-loom | ☐ _____ | |
| | | | | ☐ Round | ☐ Long | |
| | | | | ☐ S-loom | ☐ _____ | |
| | | | | ☐ Round | ☐ Long | |
| | | | | ☐ S-loom | ☐ _____ | |
| | | | | ☐ Round | ☐ Long | |
| | | | | ☐ S-loom | ☐ _____ | |
| | | | | ☐ Round | ☐ Long | |
| | | | | ☐ S-loom | ☐ _____ | |
| | | | | ☐ Round | ☐ Long | |
| | | | | ☐ S-loom | ☐ _____ | |
| | | | | ☐ Round | ☐ Long | |
| | | | | ☐ S-loom | ☐ _____ | |
| | | | | ☐ Round | ☐ Long | |
| | | | | ☐ S-loom | ☐ _____ | |
| | | | | ☐ Round | ☐ Long | |
| | | | | ☐ S-loom | ☐ _____ | |
| | | | | ☐ Round | ☐ Long | |
| | | | | ☐ S-loom | ☐ _____ | |

### Loom Gauge Reference with Center to Center Peg Measurement (in.)

| | | | | | |
|---|---|---|---|---|---|
| EFG - Extra Fine Gauge | $3/16$ | SG - Small Gauge | $5/16$, $3/8$, $7/16$ | LG - Large Gauge | $5/8$, $11/16$ |
| FG - Fine Gauge | $1/4$ | RG - Regular Gauge | $1/2$, $9/16$ | XLG - Extra Large Gauge | $3/4$, $13/16$, $7/8$, $15/16$ |
| | | | | JUMBO - Jumbo Gauge | +/- $1 1/2$ |

**INVENTORY**

Knit & Crochet Planner  goodknitkisses.com

# LOOM INVENTORY

| Brand | Gauge | Peg Spacing | # of Pegs | Type | | Other (Material, Color, ...) |
|-------|-------|-------------|-----------|------|------|------------------------------|
| | | | | ☐ Round | ☐ Long | |
| | | | | ☐ S-loom | ☐ _____ | |
| | | | | ☐ Round | ☐ Long | |
| | | | | ☐ S-loom | ☐ _____ | |
| | | | | ☐ Round | ☐ Long | |
| | | | | ☐ S-loom | ☐ _____ | |
| | | | | ☐ Round | ☐ Long | |
| | | | | ☐ S-loom | ☐ _____ | |
| | | | | ☐ Round | ☐ Long | |
| | | | | ☐ S-loom | ☐ _____ | |
| | | | | ☐ Round | ☐ Long | |
| | | | | ☐ S-loom | ☐ _____ | |
| | | | | ☐ Round | ☐ Long | |
| | | | | ☐ S-loom | ☐ _____ | |
| | | | | ☐ Round | ☐ Long | |
| | | | | ☐ S-loom | ☐ _____ | |
| | | | | ☐ Round | ☐ Long | |
| | | | | ☐ S-loom | ☐ _____ | |
| | | | | ☐ Round | ☐ Long | |
| | | | | ☐ S-loom | ☐ _____ | |
| | | | | ☐ Round | ☐ Long | |
| | | | | ☐ S-loom | ☐ _____ | |
| | | | | ☐ Round | ☐ Long | |
| | | | | ☐ S-loom | ☐ _____ | |
| | | | | ☐ Round | ☐ Long | |
| | | | | ☐ S-loom | ☐ _____ | |
| | | | | ☐ Round | ☐ Long | |
| | | | | ☐ S-loom | ☐ _____ | |

## Loom Gauge Reference with Center to Center Peg Measurement (in.)

| | | | | | |
|---|---|---|---|---|---|
| EFG - Extra Fine Gauge | $3/16$ | SG - Small Gauge | $5/16$, $3/8$, $7/16$ | LG - Large Gauge | $5/8$, $11/16$ |
| FG - Fine Gauge | $1/4$ | RG - Regular Gauge | $1/2$, $9/16$ | XLG - Extra Large Gauge | $3/4$, $13/16$, $7/8$, $15/16$ |
| | | | | JUMBO - Jumbo Gauge | +/- $1 1/2$ |

Knit & Crochet Planner  goodknitkisses.com

# LOOM INVENTORY

| Brand | Gauge | Peg Spacing | # of Pegs | Type | | Other (Material, Color, …) |
|---|---|---|---|---|---|---|
| | | | | ☐ Round | ☐ Long | |
| | | | | ☐ S-loom | ☐ _____ | |
| | | | | ☐ Round | ☐ Long | |
| | | | | ☐ S-loom | ☐ _____ | |
| | | | | ☐ Round | ☐ Long | |
| | | | | ☐ S-loom | ☐ _____ | |
| | | | | ☐ Round | ☐ Long | |
| | | | | ☐ S-loom | ☐ _____ | |
| | | | | ☐ Round | ☐ Long | |
| | | | | ☐ S-loom | ☐ _____ | |
| | | | | ☐ Round | ☐ Long | |
| | | | | ☐ S-loom | ☐ _____ | |
| | | | | ☐ Round | ☐ Long | |
| | | | | ☐ S-loom | ☐ _____ | |
| | | | | ☐ Round | ☐ Long | |
| | | | | ☐ S-loom | ☐ _____ | |
| | | | | ☐ Round | ☐ Long | |
| | | | | ☐ S-loom | ☐ _____ | |
| | | | | ☐ Round | ☐ Long | |
| | | | | ☐ S-loom | ☐ _____ | |
| | | | | ☐ Round | ☐ Long | |
| | | | | ☐ S-loom | ☐ _____ | |
| | | | | ☐ Round | ☐ Long | |
| | | | | ☐ S-loom | ☐ _____ | |
| | | | | ☐ Round | ☐ Long | |
| | | | | ☐ S-loom | ☐ _____ | |
| | | | | ☐ Round | ☐ Long | |
| | | | | ☐ S-loom | ☐ _____ | |

## Loom Gauge Reference with Center to Center Peg Measurement (in.)

| | | | | | |
|---|---|---|---|---|---|
| EFG - Extra Fine Gauge | $\frac{3}{16}$ | SG - Small Gauge | $\frac{5}{16}, \frac{3}{8}, \frac{7}{16}$ | LG - Large Gauge | $\frac{5}{8}, \frac{11}{16}$ |
| FG - Fine Gauge | $\frac{1}{4}$ | RG - Regular Gauge | $\frac{1}{2}, \frac{9}{16}$ | XLG - Extra Large Gauge | $\frac{3}{4}, \frac{13}{16}, \frac{7}{8}, \frac{15}{16}$ |
| | | | | JUMBO - Jumbo Gauge | $+/- 1\frac{1}{2}$ |

INVENTORY

# STRAIGHT NEEDLE INVENTORY

| Brand/Type | Size US | mm | Length | Material | Other (Color...) |
|---|---|---|---|---|---|
| | | | | ☐ Metal ☐ Wood<br>☐ Plastic ☐ _____ | |
| | | | | ☐ Metal ☐ Wood<br>☐ Plastic ☐ _____ | |
| | | | | ☐ Metal ☐ Wood<br>☐ Plastic ☐ _____ | |
| | | | | ☐ Metal ☐ Wood<br>☐ Plastic ☐ _____ | |
| | | | | ☐ Metal ☐ Wood<br>☐ Plastic ☐ _____ | |
| | | | | ☐ Metal ☐ Wood<br>☐ Plastic ☐ _____ | |
| | | | | ☐ Metal ☐ Wood<br>☐ Plastic ☐ _____ | |
| | | | | ☐ Metal ☐ Wood<br>☐ Plastic ☐ _____ | |
| | | | | ☐ Metal ☐ Wood<br>☐ Plastic ☐ _____ | |
| | | | | ☐ Metal ☐ Wood<br>☐ Plastic ☐ _____ | |
| | | | | ☐ Metal ☐ Wood<br>☐ Plastic ☐ _____ | |
| | | | | ☐ Metal ☐ Wood<br>☐ Plastic ☐ _____ | |
| | | | | ☐ Metal ☐ Wood<br>☐ Plastic ☐ _____ | |
| | | | | ☐ Metal ☐ Wood<br>☐ Plastic ☐ _____ | |
| | | | | ☐ Metal ☐ Wood<br>☐ Plastic ☐ _____ | |
| | | | | ☐ Metal ☐ Wood<br>☐ Plastic ☐ _____ | |
| | | | | ☐ Metal ☐ Wood<br>☐ Plastic ☐ _____ | |

INVENTORY

Knit & Crochet Planner

goodknitkisses.com

# STRAIGHT NEEDLE INVENTORY

| Brand/Type | Size US | Size mm | Length | Material | Other (Color...) |
|---|---|---|---|---|---|
| | | | | ☐ Metal  ☐ Wood<br>☐ Plastic  ☐ _____ | |
| | | | | ☐ Metal  ☐ Wood<br>☐ Plastic  ☐ _____ | |
| | | | | ☐ Metal  ☐ Wood<br>☐ Plastic  ☐ _____ | |
| | | | | ☐ Metal  ☐ Wood<br>☐ Plastic  ☐ _____ | |
| | | | | ☐ Metal  ☐ Wood<br>☐ Plastic  ☐ _____ | |
| | | | | ☐ Metal  ☐ Wood<br>☐ Plastic  ☐ _____ | |
| | | | | ☐ Metal  ☐ Wood<br>☐ Plastic  ☐ _____ | |
| | | | | ☐ Metal  ☐ Wood<br>☐ Plastic  ☐ _____ | |
| | | | | ☐ Metal  ☐ Wood<br>☐ Plastic  ☐ _____ | |
| | | | | ☐ Metal  ☐ Wood<br>☐ Plastic  ☐ _____ | |
| | | | | ☐ Metal  ☐ Wood<br>☐ Plastic  ☐ _____ | |
| | | | | ☐ Metal  ☐ Wood<br>☐ Plastic  ☐ _____ | |
| | | | | ☐ Metal  ☐ Wood<br>☐ Plastic  ☐ _____ | |
| | | | | ☐ Metal  ☐ Wood<br>☐ Plastic  ☐ _____ | |
| | | | | ☐ Metal  ☐ Wood<br>☐ Plastic  ☐ _____ | |
| | | | | ☐ Metal  ☐ Wood<br>☐ Plastic  ☐ _____ | |
| | | | | ☐ Metal  ☐ Wood<br>☐ Plastic  ☐ _____ | |

INVENTORY

Knit & Crochet Planner  goodknitkisses.com

# STRAIGHT NEEDLE INVENTORY

| Brand/Type | Size US | Size mm | Length | Material | Other (Color...) |
|---|---|---|---|---|---|
| | | | | ☐ Metal  ☐ Wood<br>☐ Plastic  ☐ _____ | |
| | | | | ☐ Metal  ☐ Wood<br>☐ Plastic  ☐ _____ | |
| | | | | ☐ Metal  ☐ Wood<br>☐ Plastic  ☐ _____ | |
| | | | | ☐ Metal  ☐ Wood<br>☐ Plastic  ☐ _____ | |
| | | | | ☐ Metal  ☐ Wood<br>☐ Plastic  ☐ _____ | |
| | | | | ☐ Metal  ☐ Wood<br>☐ Plastic  ☐ _____ | |
| | | | | ☐ Metal  ☐ Wood<br>☐ Plastic  ☐ _____ | |
| | | | | ☐ Metal  ☐ Wood<br>☐ Plastic  ☐ _____ | |
| | | | | ☐ Metal  ☐ Wood<br>☐ Plastic  ☐ _____ | |
| | | | | ☐ Metal  ☐ Wood<br>☐ Plastic  ☐ _____ | |
| | | | | ☐ Metal  ☐ Wood<br>☐ Plastic  ☐ _____ | |
| | | | | ☐ Metal  ☐ Wood<br>☐ Plastic  ☐ _____ | |
| | | | | ☐ Metal  ☐ Wood<br>☐ Plastic  ☐ _____ | |
| | | | | ☐ Metal  ☐ Wood<br>☐ Plastic  ☐ _____ | |
| | | | | ☐ Metal  ☐ Wood<br>☐ Plastic  ☐ _____ | |
| | | | | ☐ Metal  ☐ Wood<br>☐ Plastic  ☐ _____ | |

INVENTORY

Knit & Crochet Planner

goodknitkisses.com

# STRAIGHT NEEDLE INVENTORY

| Brand/Type | Size US | mm | Length | Material | Other (Color...) |
|---|---|---|---|---|---|
| | | | | ☐ Metal ☐ Wood<br>☐ Plastic ☐ _____ | |
| | | | | ☐ Metal ☐ Wood<br>☐ Plastic ☐ _____ | |
| | | | | ☐ Metal ☐ Wood<br>☐ Plastic ☐ _____ | |
| | | | | ☐ Metal ☐ Wood<br>☐ Plastic ☐ _____ | |
| | | | | ☐ Metal ☐ Wood<br>☐ Plastic ☐ _____ | |
| | | | | ☐ Metal ☐ Wood<br>☐ Plastic ☐ _____ | |
| | | | | ☐ Metal ☐ Wood<br>☐ Plastic ☐ _____ | |
| | | | | ☐ Metal ☐ Wood<br>☐ Plastic ☐ _____ | |
| | | | | ☐ Metal ☐ Wood<br>☐ Plastic ☐ _____ | |
| | | | | ☐ Metal ☐ Wood<br>☐ Plastic ☐ _____ | |
| | | | | ☐ Metal ☐ Wood<br>☐ Plastic ☐ _____ | |
| | | | | ☐ Metal ☐ Wood<br>☐ Plastic ☐ _____ | |
| | | | | ☐ Metal ☐ Wood<br>☐ Plastic ☐ _____ | |
| | | | | ☐ Metal ☐ Wood<br>☐ Plastic ☐ _____ | |
| | | | | ☐ Metal ☐ Wood<br>☐ Plastic ☐ _____ | |
| | | | | ☐ Metal ☐ Wood<br>☐ Plastic ☐ _____ | |

INVENTORY

# CIRCULAR NEEDLE INVENTORY

| Brand | Size US | Size mm | Cable Length | Material | | Type | Other (color...) |
|---|---|---|---|---|---|---|---|
| | | | | ☐ Metal ☐ Wood | ☐ Plastic ☐ _____ | ☐ Interchangeable ☐ Fixed | |
| | | | | ☐ Metal ☐ Wood | ☐ Plastic ☐ _____ | ☐ Interchangeable ☐ Fixed | |
| | | | | ☐ Metal ☐ Wood | ☐ Plastic ☐ _____ | ☐ Interchangeable ☐ Fixed | |
| | | | | ☐ Metal ☐ Wood | ☐ Plastic ☐ _____ | ☐ Interchangeable ☐ Fixed | |
| | | | | ☐ Metal ☐ Wood | ☐ Plastic ☐ _____ | ☐ Interchangeable ☐ Fixed | |
| | | | | ☐ Metal ☐ Wood | ☐ Plastic ☐ _____ | ☐ Interchangeable ☐ Fixed | |
| | | | | ☐ Metal ☐ Wood | ☐ Plastic ☐ _____ | ☐ Interchangeable ☐ Fixed | |
| | | | | ☐ Metal ☐ Wood | ☐ Plastic ☐ _____ | ☐ Interchangeable ☐ Fixed | |
| | | | | ☐ Metal ☐ Wood | ☐ Plastic ☐ _____ | ☐ Interchangeable ☐ Fixed | |
| | | | | ☐ Metal ☐ Wood | ☐ Plastic ☐ _____ | ☐ Interchangeable ☐ Fixed | |
| | | | | ☐ Metal ☐ Wood | ☐ Plastic ☐ _____ | ☐ Interchangeable ☐ Fixed | |
| | | | | ☐ Metal ☐ Wood | ☐ Plastic ☐ _____ | ☐ Interchangeable ☐ Fixed | |
| | | | | ☐ Metal ☐ Wood | ☐ Plastic ☐ _____ | ☐ Interchangeable ☐ Fixed | |
| | | | | ☐ Metal ☐ Wood | ☐ Plastic ☐ _____ | ☐ Interchangeable ☐ Fixed | |
| | | | | ☐ Metal ☐ Wood | ☐ Plastic ☐ _____ | ☐ Interchangeable ☐ Fixed | |
| | | | | ☐ Metal ☐ Wood | ☐ Plastic ☐ _____ | ☐ Interchangeable ☐ Fixed | |
| | | | | ☐ Metal ☐ Wood | ☐ Plastic ☐ _____ | ☐ Interchangeable ☐ Fixed | |

Knit & Crochet Planner  goodknitkisses.com

# CIRCULAR NEEDLE INVENTORY

| Brand | Size US | mm | Cable Length | Material | | Type | Other (color...) |
|---|---|---|---|---|---|---|---|
| | | | | ☐ Metal ☐ Wood<br>☐ Plastic ☐ _____ | | ☐ Interchangeable<br>☐ Fixed | |
| | | | | ☐ Metal ☐ Wood<br>☐ Plastic ☐ _____ | | ☐ Interchangeable<br>☐ Fixed | |
| | | | | ☐ Metal ☐ Wood<br>☐ Plastic ☐ _____ | | ☐ Interchangeable<br>☐ Fixed | |
| | | | | ☐ Metal ☐ Wood<br>☐ Plastic ☐ _____ | | ☐ Interchangeable<br>☐ Fixed | |
| | | | | ☐ Metal ☐ Wood<br>☐ Plastic ☐ _____ | | ☐ Interchangeable<br>☐ Fixed | |
| | | | | ☐ Metal ☐ Wood<br>☐ Plastic ☐ _____ | | ☐ Interchangeable<br>☐ Fixed | |
| | | | | ☐ Metal ☐ Wood<br>☐ Plastic ☐ _____ | | ☐ Interchangeable<br>☐ Fixed | |
| | | | | ☐ Metal ☐ Wood<br>☐ Plastic ☐ _____ | | ☐ Interchangeable<br>☐ Fixed | |
| | | | | ☐ Metal ☐ Wood<br>☐ Plastic ☐ _____ | | ☐ Interchangeable<br>☐ Fixed | |
| | | | | ☐ Metal ☐ Wood<br>☐ Plastic ☐ _____ | | ☐ Interchangeable<br>☐ Fixed | |
| | | | | ☐ Metal ☐ Wood<br>☐ Plastic ☐ _____ | | ☐ Interchangeable<br>☐ Fixed | |
| | | | | ☐ Metal ☐ Wood<br>☐ Plastic ☐ _____ | | ☐ Interchangeable<br>☐ Fixed | |
| | | | | ☐ Metal ☐ Wood<br>☐ Plastic ☐ _____ | | ☐ Interchangeable<br>☐ Fixed | |
| | | | | ☐ Metal ☐ Wood<br>☐ Plastic ☐ _____ | | ☐ Interchangeable<br>☐ Fixed | |
| | | | | ☐ Metal ☐ Wood<br>☐ Plastic ☐ _____ | | ☐ Interchangeable<br>☐ Fixed | |
| | | | | ☐ Metal ☐ Wood<br>☐ Plastic ☐ _____ | | ☐ Interchangeable<br>☐ Fixed | |

INVENTORY

Knit & Crochet Planner

goodknitkisses.com

# CIRCULAR NEEDLE INVENTORY

| Brand | Size US | Size mm | Cable Length | Material | | Type | Other (color...) |
|---|---|---|---|---|---|---|---|
| | | | | ☐ Metal ☐ Wood | ☐ Plastic ☐ _____ | ☐ Interchangeable ☐ Fixed | |
| | | | | ☐ Metal ☐ Wood | ☐ Plastic ☐ _____ | ☐ Interchangeable ☐ Fixed | |
| | | | | ☐ Metal ☐ Wood | ☐ Plastic ☐ _____ | ☐ Interchangeable ☐ Fixed | |
| | | | | ☐ Metal ☐ Wood | ☐ Plastic ☐ _____ | ☐ Interchangeable ☐ Fixed | |
| | | | | ☐ Metal ☐ Wood | ☐ Plastic ☐ _____ | ☐ Interchangeable ☐ Fixed | |
| | | | | ☐ Metal ☐ Wood | ☐ Plastic ☐ _____ | ☐ Interchangeable ☐ Fixed | |
| | | | | ☐ Metal ☐ Wood | ☐ Plastic ☐ _____ | ☐ Interchangeable ☐ Fixed | |
| | | | | ☐ Metal ☐ Wood | ☐ Plastic ☐ _____ | ☐ Interchangeable ☐ Fixed | |
| | | | | ☐ Metal ☐ Wood | ☐ Plastic ☐ _____ | ☐ Interchangeable ☐ Fixed | |
| | | | | ☐ Metal ☐ Wood | ☐ Plastic ☐ _____ | ☐ Interchangeable ☐ Fixed | |
| | | | | ☐ Metal ☐ Wood | ☐ Plastic ☐ _____ | ☐ Interchangeable ☐ Fixed | |
| | | | | ☐ Metal ☐ Wood | ☐ Plastic ☐ _____ | ☐ Interchangeable ☐ Fixed | |
| | | | | ☐ Metal ☐ Wood | ☐ Plastic ☐ _____ | ☐ Interchangeable ☐ Fixed | |
| | | | | ☐ Metal ☐ Wood | ☐ Plastic ☐ _____ | ☐ Interchangeable ☐ Fixed | |
| | | | | ☐ Metal ☐ Wood | ☐ Plastic ☐ _____ | ☐ Interchangeable ☐ Fixed | |
| | | | | ☐ Metal ☐ Wood | ☐ Plastic ☐ _____ | ☐ Interchangeable ☐ Fixed | |
| | | | | ☐ Metal ☐ Wood | ☐ Plastic ☐ _____ | ☐ Interchangeable ☐ Fixed | |

**INVENTORY**

# CIRCULAR NEEDLE INVENTORY

| Brand | Size US | Size mm | Cable Length | Material | | Type | Other (color...) |
|-------|---------|---------|--------------|----------|---|------|------------------|
| | | | | ☐ Metal  ☐ Wood<br>☐ Plastic  ☐ _____ | | ☐ Interchangeable<br>☐ Fixed | |
| | | | | ☐ Metal  ☐ Wood<br>☐ Plastic  ☐ _____ | | ☐ Interchangeable<br>☐ Fixed | |
| | | | | ☐ Metal  ☐ Wood<br>☐ Plastic  ☐ _____ | | ☐ Interchangeable<br>☐ Fixed | |
| | | | | ☐ Metal  ☐ Wood<br>☐ Plastic  ☐ _____ | | ☐ Interchangeable<br>☐ Fixed | |
| | | | | ☐ Metal  ☐ Wood<br>☐ Plastic  ☐ _____ | | ☐ Interchangeable<br>☐ Fixed | |
| | | | | ☐ Metal  ☐ Wood<br>☐ Plastic  ☐ _____ | | ☐ Interchangeable<br>☐ Fixed | |
| | | | | ☐ Metal  ☐ Wood<br>☐ Plastic  ☐ _____ | | ☐ Interchangeable<br>☐ Fixed | |
| | | | | ☐ Metal  ☐ Wood<br>☐ Plastic  ☐ _____ | | ☐ Interchangeable<br>☐ Fixed | |
| | | | | ☐ Metal  ☐ Wood<br>☐ Plastic  ☐ _____ | | ☐ Interchangeable<br>☐ Fixed | |
| | | | | ☐ Metal  ☐ Wood<br>☐ Plastic  ☐ _____ | | ☐ Interchangeable<br>☐ Fixed | |
| | | | | ☐ Metal  ☐ Wood<br>☐ Plastic  ☐ _____ | | ☐ Interchangeable<br>☐ Fixed | |
| | | | | ☐ Metal  ☐ Wood<br>☐ Plastic  ☐ _____ | | ☐ Interchangeable<br>☐ Fixed | |
| | | | | ☐ Metal  ☐ Wood<br>☐ Plastic  ☐ _____ | | ☐ Interchangeable<br>☐ Fixed | |
| | | | | ☐ Metal  ☐ Wood<br>☐ Plastic  ☐ _____ | | ☐ Interchangeable<br>☐ Fixed | |
| | | | | ☐ Metal  ☐ Wood<br>☐ Plastic  ☐ _____ | | ☐ Interchangeable<br>☐ Fixed | |
| | | | | ☐ Metal  ☐ Wood<br>☐ Plastic  ☐ _____ | | ☐ Interchangeable<br>☐ Fixed | |
| | | | | ☐ Metal  ☐ Wood<br>☐ Plastic  ☐ _____ | | ☐ Interchangeable<br>☐ Fixed | |

# CIRCULAR NEEDLE INVENTORY

| Brand | Size US | mm | Cable Length | Material | | Type | Other (color...) |
|---|---|---|---|---|---|---|---|
| | | | | ☐ Metal ☐ Wood<br>☐ Plastic ☐ _____ | | ☐ Interchangeable<br>☐ Fixed | |
| | | | | ☐ Metal ☐ Wood<br>☐ Plastic ☐ _____ | | ☐ Interchangeable<br>☐ Fixed | |
| | | | | ☐ Metal ☐ Wood<br>☐ Plastic ☐ _____ | | ☐ Interchangeable<br>☐ Fixed | |
| | | | | ☐ Metal ☐ Wood<br>☐ Plastic ☐ _____ | | ☐ Interchangeable<br>☐ Fixed | |
| | | | | ☐ Metal ☐ Wood<br>☐ Plastic ☐ _____ | | ☐ Interchangeable<br>☐ Fixed | |
| | | | | ☐ Metal ☐ Wood<br>☐ Plastic ☐ _____ | | ☐ Interchangeable<br>☐ Fixed | |
| | | | | ☐ Metal ☐ Wood<br>☐ Plastic ☐ _____ | | ☐ Interchangeable<br>☐ Fixed | |
| | | | | ☐ Metal ☐ Wood<br>☐ Plastic ☐ _____ | | ☐ Interchangeable<br>☐ Fixed | |
| | | | | ☐ Metal ☐ Wood<br>☐ Plastic ☐ _____ | | ☐ Interchangeable<br>☐ Fixed | |
| | | | | ☐ Metal ☐ Wood<br>☐ Plastic ☐ _____ | | ☐ Interchangeable<br>☐ Fixed | |
| | | | | ☐ Metal ☐ Wood<br>☐ Plastic ☐ _____ | | ☐ Interchangeable<br>☐ Fixed | |
| | | | | ☐ Metal ☐ Wood<br>☐ Plastic ☐ _____ | | ☐ Interchangeable<br>☐ Fixed | |
| | | | | ☐ Metal ☐ Wood<br>☐ Plastic ☐ _____ | | ☐ Interchangeable<br>☐ Fixed | |
| | | | | ☐ Metal ☐ Wood<br>☐ Plastic ☐ _____ | | ☐ Interchangeable<br>☐ Fixed | |
| | | | | ☐ Metal ☐ Wood<br>☐ Plastic ☐ _____ | | ☐ Interchangeable<br>☐ Fixed | |
| | | | | ☐ Metal ☐ Wood<br>☐ Plastic ☐ _____ | | ☐ Interchangeable<br>☐ Fixed | |
| | | | | ☐ Metal ☐ Wood<br>☐ Plastic ☐ _____ | | ☐ Interchangeable<br>☐ Fixed | |

Knit & Crochet Planner  goodknitkisses.com

# CIRCULAR NEEDLE INVENTORY

| Brand | Size US | Size mm | Cable Length | Material | | Type | Other (color...) |
|-------|---------|---------|--------------|----------|---|------|------------------|
| | | | | ☐ Metal ☐ Wood<br>☐ Plastic ☐ _____ | | ☐ Interchangeable<br>☐ Fixed | |
| | | | | ☐ Metal ☐ Wood<br>☐ Plastic ☐ _____ | | ☐ Interchangeable<br>☐ Fixed | |
| | | | | ☐ Metal ☐ Wood<br>☐ Plastic ☐ _____ | | ☐ Interchangeable<br>☐ Fixed | |
| | | | | ☐ Metal ☐ Wood<br>☐ Plastic ☐ _____ | | ☐ Interchangeable<br>☐ Fixed | |
| | | | | ☐ Metal ☐ Wood<br>☐ Plastic ☐ _____ | | ☐ Interchangeable<br>☐ Fixed | |
| | | | | ☐ Metal ☐ Wood<br>☐ Plastic ☐ _____ | | ☐ Interchangeable<br>☐ Fixed | |
| | | | | ☐ Metal ☐ Wood<br>☐ Plastic ☐ _____ | | ☐ Interchangeable<br>☐ Fixed | |
| | | | | ☐ Metal ☐ Wood<br>☐ Plastic ☐ _____ | | ☐ Interchangeable<br>☐ Fixed | |
| | | | | ☐ Metal ☐ Wood<br>☐ Plastic ☐ _____ | | ☐ Interchangeable<br>☐ Fixed | |
| | | | | ☐ Metal ☐ Wood<br>☐ Plastic ☐ _____ | | ☐ Interchangeable<br>☐ Fixed | |
| | | | | ☐ Metal ☐ Wood<br>☐ Plastic ☐ _____ | | ☐ Interchangeable<br>☐ Fixed | |
| | | | | ☐ Metal ☐ Wood<br>☐ Plastic ☐ _____ | | ☐ Interchangeable<br>☐ Fixed | |
| | | | | ☐ Metal ☐ Wood<br>☐ Plastic ☐ _____ | | ☐ Interchangeable<br>☐ Fixed | |
| | | | | ☐ Metal ☐ Wood<br>☐ Plastic ☐ _____ | | ☐ Interchangeable<br>☐ Fixed | |
| | | | | ☐ Metal ☐ Wood<br>☐ Plastic ☐ _____ | | ☐ Interchangeable<br>☐ Fixed | |
| | | | | ☐ Metal ☐ Wood<br>☐ Plastic ☐ _____ | | ☐ Interchangeable<br>☐ Fixed | |
| | | | | ☐ Metal ☐ Wood<br>☐ Plastic ☐ _____ | | ☐ Interchangeable<br>☐ Fixed | |

INVENTORY

Knit & Crochet Planner  goodknitkisses.com

# DPN INVENTORY

| Brand/Type | Size US | Size mm | Length | # of needles | Material | Other (Color...) |
|---|---|---|---|---|---|---|
| | | | | | ☐ Metal ☐ Wood<br>☐ Plastic ☐ _____ | |
| | | | | | ☐ Metal ☐ Wood<br>☐ Plastic ☐ _____ | |
| | | | | | ☐ Metal ☐ Wood<br>☐ Plastic ☐ _____ | |
| | | | | | ☐ Metal ☐ Wood<br>☐ Plastic ☐ _____ | |
| | | | | | ☐ Metal ☐ Wood<br>☐ Plastic ☐ _____ | |
| | | | | | ☐ Metal ☐ Wood<br>☐ Plastic ☐ _____ | |
| | | | | | ☐ Metal ☐ Wood<br>☐ Plastic ☐ _____ | |
| | | | | | ☐ Metal ☐ Wood<br>☐ Plastic ☐ _____ | |
| | | | | | ☐ Metal ☐ Wood<br>☐ Plastic ☐ _____ | |
| | | | | | ☐ Metal ☐ Wood<br>☐ Plastic ☐ _____ | |
| | | | | | ☐ Metal ☐ Wood<br>☐ Plastic ☐ _____ | |
| | | | | | ☐ Metal ☐ Wood<br>☐ Plastic ☐ _____ | |
| | | | | | ☐ Metal ☐ Wood<br>☐ Plastic ☐ _____ | |
| | | | | | ☐ Metal ☐ Wood<br>☐ Plastic ☐ _____ | |
| | | | | | ☐ Metal ☐ Wood<br>☐ Plastic ☐ _____ | |
| | | | | | ☐ Metal ☐ Wood<br>☐ Plastic ☐ _____ | |

Knit & Crochet Planner  goodknitkisses.com

# DPN INVENTORY

| Brand/Type | Size US | mm | Length | # of needles | Material | | Other (Color...) |
|---|---|---|---|---|---|---|---|
| | | | | | ☐ Metal   ☐ Wood<br>☐ Plastic  ☐ _____ | | |
| | | | | | ☐ Metal   ☐ Wood<br>☐ Plastic  ☐ _____ | | |
| | | | | | ☐ Metal   ☐ Wood<br>☐ Plastic  ☐ _____ | | |
| | | | | | ☐ Metal   ☐ Wood<br>☐ Plastic  ☐ _____ | | |
| | | | | | ☐ Metal   ☐ Wood<br>☐ Plastic  ☐ _____ | | |
| | | | | | ☐ Metal   ☐ Wood<br>☐ Plastic  ☐ _____ | | |
| | | | | | ☐ Metal   ☐ Wood<br>☐ Plastic  ☐ _____ | | |
| | | | | | ☐ Metal   ☐ Wood<br>☐ Plastic  ☐ _____ | | |
| | | | | | ☐ Metal   ☐ Wood<br>☐ Plastic  ☐ _____ | | |
| | | | | | ☐ Metal   ☐ Wood<br>☐ Plastic  ☐ _____ | | |
| | | | | | ☐ Metal   ☐ Wood<br>☐ Plastic  ☐ _____ | | |
| | | | | | ☐ Metal   ☐ Wood<br>☐ Plastic  ☐ _____ | | |
| | | | | | ☐ Metal   ☐ Wood<br>☐ Plastic  ☐ _____ | | |
| | | | | | ☐ Metal   ☐ Wood<br>☐ Plastic  ☐ _____ | | |
| | | | | | ☐ Metal   ☐ Wood<br>☐ Plastic  ☐ _____ | | |
| | | | | | ☐ Metal   ☐ Wood<br>☐ Plastic  ☐ _____ | | |

INVENTORY

# DPN INVENTORY

| Brand/Type | Size US | Size mm | Length | # of needles | Material | Other (Color...) |
|---|---|---|---|---|---|---|
| | | | | | ☐ Metal  ☐ Wood<br>☐ Plastic  ☐ _____ | |
| | | | | | ☐ Metal  ☐ Wood<br>☐ Plastic  ☐ _____ | |
| | | | | | ☐ Metal  ☐ Wood<br>☐ Plastic  ☐ _____ | |
| | | | | | ☐ Metal  ☐ Wood<br>☐ Plastic  ☐ _____ | |
| | | | | | ☐ Metal  ☐ Wood<br>☐ Plastic  ☐ _____ | |
| | | | | | ☐ Metal  ☐ Wood<br>☐ Plastic  ☐ _____ | |
| | | | | | ☐ Metal  ☐ Wood<br>☐ Plastic  ☐ _____ | |
| | | | | | ☐ Metal  ☐ Wood<br>☐ Plastic  ☐ _____ | |
| | | | | | ☐ Metal  ☐ Wood<br>☐ Plastic  ☐ _____ | |
| | | | | | ☐ Metal  ☐ Wood<br>☐ Plastic  ☐ _____ | |
| | | | | | ☐ Metal  ☐ Wood<br>☐ Plastic  ☐ _____ | |
| | | | | | ☐ Metal  ☐ Wood<br>☐ Plastic  ☐ _____ | |
| | | | | | ☐ Metal  ☐ Wood<br>☐ Plastic  ☐ _____ | |
| | | | | | ☐ Metal  ☐ Wood<br>☐ Plastic  ☐ _____ | |
| | | | | | ☐ Metal  ☐ Wood<br>☐ Plastic  ☐ _____ | |
| | | | | | ☐ Metal  ☐ Wood<br>☐ Plastic  ☐ _____ | |
| | | | | | ☐ Metal  ☐ Wood | |

Knit & Crochet Planner

goodknitkisses.com

# DPN INVENTORY

| Brand/Type | Size US | Size mm | Length | # of needles | Material | Other (Color...) |
|---|---|---|---|---|---|---|
| | | | | | ☐ Metal ☐ Wood <br> ☐ Plastic ☐ _____ | |
| | | | | | ☐ Metal ☐ Wood <br> ☐ Plastic ☐ _____ | |
| | | | | | ☐ Metal ☐ Wood <br> ☐ Plastic ☐ _____ | |
| | | | | | ☐ Metal ☐ Wood <br> ☐ Plastic ☐ _____ | |
| | | | | | ☐ Metal ☐ Wood <br> ☐ Plastic ☐ _____ | |
| | | | | | ☐ Metal ☐ Wood <br> ☐ Plastic ☐ _____ | |
| | | | | | ☐ Metal ☐ Wood <br> ☐ Plastic ☐ _____ | |
| | | | | | ☐ Metal ☐ Wood <br> ☐ Plastic ☐ _____ | |
| | | | | | ☐ Metal ☐ Wood <br> ☐ Plastic ☐ _____ | |
| | | | | | ☐ Metal ☐ Wood <br> ☐ Plastic ☐ _____ | |
| | | | | | ☐ Metal ☐ Wood <br> ☐ Plastic ☐ _____ | |
| | | | | | ☐ Metal ☐ Wood <br> ☐ Plastic ☐ _____ | |
| | | | | | ☐ Metal ☐ Wood <br> ☐ Plastic ☐ _____ | |
| | | | | | ☐ Metal ☐ Wood <br> ☐ Plastic ☐ _____ | |
| | | | | | ☐ Metal ☐ Wood <br> ☐ Plastic ☐ _____ | |
| | | | | | ☐ Metal ☐ Wood <br> ☐ Plastic ☐ _____ | |
| | | | | | ☐ Metal ☐ Wood <br> ☐ Plastic ☐ _____ | |

# CROCHET HOOK INVENTORY

| Brand/Type | Size US | Size mm | Material | | Other (Tunisian, length, color...) |
|---|---|---|---|---|---|
| | | | ☐ Aluminum ☐ Plastic | ☐ Bamboo ☐ _____ | |
| | | | ☐ Aluminum ☐ Plastic | ☐ Bamboo ☐ _____ | |
| | | | ☐ Aluminum ☐ Plastic | ☐ Bamboo ☐ _____ | |
| | | | ☐ Aluminum ☐ Plastic | ☐ Bamboo ☐ _____ | |
| | | | ☐ Aluminum ☐ Plastic | ☐ Bamboo ☐ _____ | |
| | | | ☐ Aluminum ☐ Plastic | ☐ Bamboo ☐ _____ | |
| | | | ☐ Aluminum ☐ Plastic | ☐ Bamboo ☐ _____ | |
| | | | ☐ Aluminum ☐ Plastic | ☐ Bamboo ☐ _____ | |
| | | | ☐ Aluminum ☐ Plastic | ☐ Bamboo ☐ _____ | |
| | | | ☐ Aluminum ☐ Plastic | ☐ Bamboo ☐ _____ | |
| | | | ☐ Aluminum ☐ Plastic | ☐ Bamboo ☐ _____ | |
| | | | ☐ Aluminum ☐ Plastic | ☐ Bamboo ☐ _____ | |
| | | | ☐ Aluminum ☐ Plastic | ☐ Bamboo ☐ _____ | |
| | | | ☐ Aluminum ☐ Plastic | ☐ Bamboo ☐ _____ | |
| | | | ☐ Aluminum ☐ Plastic | ☐ Bamboo ☐ _____ | |
| | | | ☐ Aluminum ☐ Plastic | ☐ Bamboo ☐ _____ | |

INVENTORY

# CROCHET HOOK INVENTORY

| Brand/Type | Size US | mm | Material | Other (Tunisian, length, color...) |
|---|---|---|---|---|
| | | | ☐ Aluminum  ☐ Bamboo<br>☐ Plastic  ☐ _____ | |
| | | | ☐ Aluminum  ☐ Bamboo<br>☐ Plastic  ☐ _____ | |
| | | | ☐ Aluminum  ☐ Bamboo<br>☐ Plastic  ☐ _____ | |
| | | | ☐ Aluminum  ☐ Bamboo<br>☐ Plastic  ☐ _____ | |
| | | | ☐ Aluminum  ☐ Bamboo<br>☐ Plastic  ☐ _____ | |
| | | | ☐ Aluminum  ☐ Bamboo<br>☐ Plastic  ☐ _____ | |
| | | | ☐ Aluminum  ☐ Bamboo<br>☐ Plastic  ☐ _____ | |
| | | | ☐ Aluminum  ☐ Bamboo<br>☐ Plastic  ☐ _____ | |
| | | | ☐ Aluminum  ☐ Bamboo<br>☐ Plastic  ☐ _____ | |
| | | | ☐ Aluminum  ☐ Bamboo<br>☐ Plastic  ☐ _____ | |
| | | | ☐ Aluminum  ☐ Bamboo<br>☐ Plastic  ☐ _____ | |
| | | | ☐ Aluminum  ☐ Bamboo<br>☐ Plastic  ☐ _____ | |
| | | | ☐ Aluminum  ☐ Bamboo<br>☐ Plastic  ☐ _____ | |
| | | | ☐ Aluminum  ☐ Bamboo<br>☐ Plastic  ☐ _____ | |
| | | | ☐ Aluminum  ☐ Bamboo<br>☐ Plastic  ☐ _____ | |

INVENTORY

Knit & Crochet Planner

goodknitkisses.com

# CROCHET HOOK INVENTORY

| Brand/Type | Size US | mm | Material | Other (Tunisian, length, color...) |
|---|---|---|---|---|
| | | | ☐ Aluminum  ☐ Bamboo<br>☐ Plastic  ☐ _____ | |
| | | | ☐ Aluminum  ☐ Bamboo<br>☐ Plastic  ☐ _____ | |
| | | | ☐ Aluminum  ☐ Bamboo<br>☐ Plastic  ☐ _____ | |
| | | | ☐ Aluminum  ☐ Bamboo<br>☐ Plastic  ☐ _____ | |
| | | | ☐ Aluminum  ☐ Bamboo<br>☐ Plastic  ☐ _____ | |
| | | | ☐ Aluminum  ☐ Bamboo<br>☐ Plastic  ☐ _____ | |
| | | | ☐ Aluminum  ☐ Bamboo<br>☐ Plastic  ☐ _____ | |
| | | | ☐ Aluminum  ☐ Bamboo<br>☐ Plastic  ☐ _____ | |
| | | | ☐ Aluminum  ☐ Bamboo<br>☐ Plastic  ☐ _____ | |
| | | | ☐ Aluminum  ☐ Bamboo<br>☐ Plastic  ☐ _____ | |
| | | | ☐ Aluminum  ☐ Bamboo<br>☐ Plastic  ☐ _____ | |
| | | | ☐ Aluminum  ☐ Bamboo<br>☐ Plastic  ☐ _____ | |
| | | | ☐ Aluminum  ☐ Bamboo<br>☐ Plastic  ☐ _____ | |
| | | | ☐ Aluminum  ☐ Bamboo<br>☐ Plastic  ☐ _____ | |
| | | | ☐ Aluminum  ☐ Bamboo<br>☐ Plastic  ☐ _____ | |
| | | | ☐ Aluminum  ☐ Bamboo<br>☐ Plastic  ☐ _____ | |

INVENTORY

Knit & Crochet Planner

goodknitkisses.com

# CROCHET HOOK INVENTORY

| Brand/Type | Size US | mm | Material | | Other (Tunisian, length, color...) |
|---|---|---|---|---|---|
| | | | ☐ Aluminum ☐ Plastic | ☐ Bamboo ☐ _____ | |
| | | | ☐ Aluminum ☐ Plastic | ☐ Bamboo ☐ _____ | |
| | | | ☐ Aluminum ☐ Plastic | ☐ Bamboo ☐ _____ | |
| | | | ☐ Aluminum ☐ Plastic | ☐ Bamboo ☐ _____ | |
| | | | ☐ Aluminum ☐ Plastic | ☐ Bamboo ☐ _____ | |
| | | | ☐ Aluminum ☐ Plastic | ☐ Bamboo ☐ _____ | |
| | | | ☐ Aluminum ☐ Plastic | ☐ Bamboo ☐ _____ | |
| | | | ☐ Aluminum ☐ Plastic | ☐ Bamboo ☐ _____ | |
| | | | ☐ Aluminum ☐ Plastic | ☐ Bamboo ☐ _____ | |
| | | | ☐ Aluminum ☐ Plastic | ☐ Bamboo ☐ _____ | |
| | | | ☐ Aluminum ☐ Plastic | ☐ Bamboo ☐ _____ | |
| | | | ☐ Aluminum ☐ Plastic | ☐ Bamboo ☐ _____ | |
| | | | ☐ Aluminum ☐ Plastic | ☐ Bamboo ☐ _____ | |
| | | | ☐ Aluminum ☐ Plastic | ☐ Bamboo ☐ _____ | |
| | | | ☐ Aluminum ☐ Plastic | ☐ Bamboo ☐ _____ | |
| | | | ☐ Aluminum | ☐ Bamboo | |

INVENTORY

# CROCHET HOOK INVENTORY

| Brand/Type | Size US | Size mm | Material | Other (Tunisian, length, color...) |
|---|---|---|---|---|
| | | | ☐ Aluminum ☐ Bamboo <br> ☐ Plastic ☐ _____ | |
| | | | ☐ Aluminum ☐ Bamboo <br> ☐ Plastic ☐ _____ | |
| | | | ☐ Aluminum ☐ Bamboo <br> ☐ Plastic ☐ _____ | |
| | | | ☐ Aluminum ☐ Bamboo <br> ☐ Plastic ☐ _____ | |
| | | | ☐ Aluminum ☐ Bamboo <br> ☐ Plastic ☐ _____ | |
| | | | ☐ Aluminum ☐ Bamboo <br> ☐ Plastic ☐ _____ | |
| | | | ☐ Aluminum ☐ Bamboo <br> ☐ Plastic ☐ _____ | |
| | | | ☐ Aluminum ☐ Bamboo <br> ☐ Plastic ☐ _____ | |
| | | | ☐ Aluminum ☐ Bamboo <br> ☐ Plastic ☐ _____ | |
| | | | ☐ Aluminum ☐ Bamboo <br> ☐ Plastic ☐ _____ | |
| | | | ☐ Aluminum ☐ Bamboo <br> ☐ Plastic ☐ _____ | |
| | | | ☐ Aluminum ☐ Bamboo <br> ☐ Plastic ☐ _____ | |
| | | | ☐ Aluminum ☐ Bamboo <br> ☐ Plastic ☐ _____ | |
| | | | ☐ Aluminum ☐ Bamboo <br> ☐ Plastic ☐ _____ | |
| | | | ☐ Aluminum ☐ Bamboo <br> ☐ Plastic ☐ _____ | |

INVENTORY

Knit & Crochet Planner  goodknitkisses.com

# CROCHET HOOK INVENTORY

| Brand/Type | Size US | mm | Material | Other (Tunisian, length, color...) |
|---|---|---|---|---|
| | | | ☐ Aluminum ☐ Bamboo<br>☐ Plastic ☐ _____ | |
| | | | ☐ Aluminum ☐ Bamboo<br>☐ Plastic ☐ _____ | |
| | | | ☐ Aluminum ☐ Bamboo<br>☐ Plastic ☐ _____ | |
| | | | ☐ Aluminum ☐ Bamboo<br>☐ Plastic ☐ _____ | |
| | | | ☐ Aluminum ☐ Bamboo<br>☐ Plastic ☐ _____ | |
| | | | ☐ Aluminum ☐ Bamboo<br>☐ Plastic ☐ _____ | |
| | | | ☐ Aluminum ☐ Bamboo<br>☐ Plastic ☐ _____ | |
| | | | ☐ Aluminum ☐ Bamboo<br>☐ Plastic ☐ _____ | |
| | | | ☐ Aluminum ☐ Bamboo<br>☐ Plastic ☐ _____ | |
| | | | ☐ Aluminum ☐ Bamboo<br>☐ Plastic ☐ _____ | |
| | | | ☐ Aluminum ☐ Bamboo<br>☐ Plastic ☐ _____ | |
| | | | ☐ Aluminum ☐ Bamboo<br>☐ Plastic ☐ _____ | |
| | | | ☐ Aluminum ☐ Bamboo<br>☐ Plastic ☐ _____ | |
| | | | ☐ Aluminum ☐ Bamboo<br>☐ Plastic ☐ _____ | |
| | | | ☐ Aluminum ☐ Bamboo<br>☐ Plastic ☐ _____ | |
| | | | ☐ Aluminum ☐ Bamboo<br>☐ Plastic ☐ _____ | |

INVENTORY

# CROCHET HOOK INVENTORY

| Brand/Type | Size US | mm | Material | Other (Tunisian, length, color...) |
|---|---|---|---|---|
| | | | ☐ Aluminum ☐ Bamboo<br>☐ Plastic ☐ _____ | |
| | | | ☐ Aluminum ☐ Bamboo<br>☐ Plastic ☐ _____ | |
| | | | ☐ Aluminum ☐ Bamboo<br>☐ Plastic ☐ _____ | |
| | | | ☐ Aluminum ☐ Bamboo<br>☐ Plastic ☐ _____ | |
| | | | ☐ Aluminum ☐ Bamboo<br>☐ Plastic ☐ _____ | |
| | | | ☐ Aluminum ☐ Bamboo<br>☐ Plastic ☐ _____ | |
| | | | ☐ Aluminum ☐ Bamboo<br>☐ Plastic ☐ _____ | |
| | | | ☐ Aluminum ☐ Bamboo<br>☐ Plastic ☐ _____ | |
| | | | ☐ Aluminum ☐ Bamboo<br>☐ Plastic ☐ _____ | |
| | | | ☐ Aluminum ☐ Bamboo<br>☐ Plastic ☐ _____ | |
| | | | ☐ Aluminum ☐ Bamboo<br>☐ Plastic ☐ _____ | |
| | | | ☐ Aluminum ☐ Bamboo<br>☐ Plastic ☐ _____ | |
| | | | ☐ Aluminum ☐ Bamboo<br>☐ Plastic ☐ _____ | |
| | | | ☐ Aluminum ☐ Bamboo<br>☐ Plastic ☐ _____ | |
| | | | ☐ Aluminum ☐ Bamboo<br>☐ Plastic ☐ _____ | |
| | | | ☐ Aluminum ☐ Bamboo<br>☐ Plastic ☐ _____ | |
| | | | ☐ Aluminum ☐ Bamboo<br>☐ Plastic ☐ _____ | |

# CROCHET HOOK INVENTORY

| Brand/Type | Size US | mm | Material | | Other (Tunisian, length, color...) |
|---|---|---|---|---|---|
| | | | ☐ Aluminum ☐ Plastic | ☐ Bamboo ☐ _____ | |
| | | | ☐ Aluminum ☐ Plastic | ☐ Bamboo ☐ _____ | |
| | | | ☐ Aluminum ☐ Plastic | ☐ Bamboo ☐ _____ | |
| | | | ☐ Aluminum ☐ Plastic | ☐ Bamboo ☐ _____ | |
| | | | ☐ Aluminum ☐ Plastic | ☐ Bamboo ☐ _____ | |
| | | | ☐ Aluminum ☐ Plastic | ☐ Bamboo ☐ _____ | |
| | | | ☐ Aluminum ☐ Plastic | ☐ Bamboo ☐ _____ | |
| | | | ☐ Aluminum ☐ Plastic | ☐ Bamboo ☐ _____ | |
| | | | ☐ Aluminum ☐ Plastic | ☐ Bamboo ☐ _____ | |
| | | | ☐ Aluminum ☐ Plastic | ☐ Bamboo ☐ _____ | |
| | | | ☐ Aluminum ☐ Plastic | ☐ Bamboo ☐ _____ | |
| | | | ☐ Aluminum ☐ Plastic | ☐ Bamboo ☐ _____ | |
| | | | ☐ Aluminum ☐ Plastic | ☐ Bamboo ☐ _____ | |
| | | | ☐ Aluminum ☐ Plastic | ☐ Bamboo ☐ _____ | |
| | | | ☐ Aluminum ☐ Plastic | ☐ Bamboo ☐ _____ | |

INVENTORY

Knit & Crochet Planner

goodknitkisses.com

CPSIA information can be obtained
at www.ICGtesting.com
Printed in the USA
LVHW060831181119
637664LV00021B/6760/P